The Heinemann Science Scheme

Foundation Edition

Byron Dawson

Heinemann Educational Publishers
Halley Court, Jordan Hill, Oxford, OX2 8EJ
Part of Harcourt Education Limited

Heinemann is the registered trademark of
Harcourt Education Limited

First published 2003

07 06 05 04 03
10 9 8 7 6 5 4 3 2 1

British Library Cataloguing in Publication Data is available from the British Library on request.

ISBN 0 435 58331 X

Edited by Ruth Holmes

Typeset by Techset Ltd, Gateshead

Original illustrations © Harcourt Education Limited 2003

Illustrated by Hardlines

Printed and bound in Italy by Printer Trento S.r.l.

Cover photo: © Science Photo Library

Picture research by Ginny Stroud Lewis

Index by Ann Hall

Acknowledgements
Every effort has been made to contact copyright holders of material reproduced in this book. Any omissions will be rectified in subsequent printings if notice is given to the publishers.

Page 135, illustration of red ball adapted from 'Make Colour Work for You', Readers Digest, published by The Readers Digest Association Limited, from the series 'The Kodak Guide to Creative Photography', 1983, copyright Kodak Limited. This volume copyright 1983 Kodak Limited, Mitchell Beazley Publishers, Salvat Editores, S.A.

The author and publishers would like to thank the following for permission to use photographs:

T = top ***B*** = bottom ***R*** = right ***L*** = left ***M*** = middle

SPL = Science Photo Library
GSF = GeoScience Photo Library

2 Peter Gould; **3 T** Peter Gould, **B** Photodisc; **4 T** Peter Gould, **B** SPL/Biophotos; **5** Alamy; **6 both and 7** Corbis; **8 all** John Frost; **11 T and M** Peter Gould; **12** Corbis; **14** SPL/Alfred Pasieka; **15** Peter Gould; **16 M** Empics, **B** SPL/Cordelia Molloy; **17 both** Peter Gould; **20** SPL/Eric Grave; **23** Corbis; **26** Peter Gould; **28 T** SPL/Dr Jeremy Burgess, **M and B** Peter Gould; **30 T** SPL, **M and B** Peter Gould; **32** SPL/Matt Meadows/Peter Arnold Inc; **34** Collections; **36** SPL; **37** SPL/Biophoto Associates; **38 all and 39** Peter Gould; **40** SPL; **42** SPL/ Saturn Stills; **44 both and 46 all** GSF; **47 T** Corbis/Papillo, **M** Corbis; **48** Andrew Lambert; **50** Heather Angel; **55 and 56 all** Peter Gould; **57** SPL; **58 T and BL** SPL, **M and BR** Peter Gould; **60 all** Peter Gould; **61 all** Peter Morris; **62 both** Peter Gould; **63 all** Peter Morris; **64** Harcourt Education; **65** Photodisc; **68 T** Corbis, **B Far and Mid L, B Far R** Harcourt Education/Gareth Boden, **B Mid R** Alamy; **69 TL and B** Peter Gould, **TM** Corbis, **TR** SPL; **71 both** Peter Gould; **74 T** Food Features, **ML** Alamy, **MR** SPL; **75 all** Peter Gould; **76 all** SPL; **77** Environmental Images; **78 TL and TR** Ginny Stroud-Lewis, **M** GSF, **B** SPL; **79 T** GSF, **M** SPL; **80 both** Corbis; **82 all** SPL; **83 both** Corbis; **84 M** Corbis, **B** SPL; **86 M** Andrew Lambert, **B** Corbis; **87 T** SPL, **M** Corbis; **88 both** GSF; **89 ML and B** GSF, **MR** Byron Dawson; **90 ML, BL and BR** GSF, **MR** SPL; **91, 92 both and 93 all** GSF; **94 T** SPL, **M and B** GSF; **95 both** GSF; **96** Andrew Lambert; **97 both** Byron Dawson; **100-102 and 106 both** Peter Gould; **107 T** Corbis/FLPA, **B** Peter Gould; **109 T** SPL, **M** Andrew Lambert; **110 T and MR** Byron Dawson, **ML** Robert Harding; **111** Peter Gould; **112** Byron Dawson; **113** SPL and Peter Morris; **114, 116-119, 121-123** Peter Gould; **124** Corbis; **132** Peter Gould; **136 BL** Corbis/Reuters, **BM** Corbis/Ted Strchinsky, **BR** Corbis/Wolfgang Kaehler; **138** Peter Gould; **142** Corbis; **144 both** Byron Dawson.

Tel: 01865 888058 email: info.he@heinemann.co.uk

Introduction

Welcome to Heinemann Science Scheme!

This is the second Foundation book in a series of three. They will cover all the science you need to learn at Key Stage 3.

The book is divided into twelve units. Each unit has several topics. A topic is on two pages. In each topic you will find:

- **Questions as you go along like this:**

  (b) What is the solute in salt solution?

  These are quick questions to check that you understand things before you carry on.

- **Questions in a box at the end of the spread with this heading:**

  QUESTIONS

  These help you bring together everything in the topic.

- **A list of key points at the end with this heading:**

  KEY POINTS

  These summarise what you have studied in the topic.

Important words are highlighted in **bold**. They are all in a glossary at the back of the book with their meanings. You can look them up as you work through the book.

As you study Heinemann Science Scheme your teacher will give you activities and extra questions from the teacher's pack. There are also tests to help you and your teachers keep track of how you're doing.

We hope you enjoy studying science with Heinemann Science Scheme.

Contents

A Food and digestion

A1 WHAT IS IN FOOD?

What are the nutrients in food?

Look at the foods in the picture.

Each food helps your body to work properly.

Some foods help you **grow**. Some foods give you **energy**.

Different foods do different jobs. This is why a healthy diet includes lots of different foods.

a Why does a healthy diet contain lots of different foods?

The things your body needs from food are called **nutrients**. Food also contains water. There are six different kinds of nutrient. They are found in different foods, as the table shows.

b Which kinds of food contain lots of vitamins?

Nutrient	Food it is found in
fat	butter, cooking oil and cream
carbohydrate	rice, bread and potatoes
protein	meat, fish and eggs
vitamins	fruit, vegetables and cereals
minerals	meat, milk and seafood
fibre	fruit, vegetables and brown bread

Which foods give you which nutrients?

Sometimes it is hard to tell which nutrients are in your food.

People who make the food use a label to tell us which nutrients are in the food. Look at the picture of the label. Foods contain mainly protein, carbohydrate, fat, fibre and water. They contain very small amounts of minerals and vitamins.

c Which nutrients are missing from the food shown on the label?

NUTRITION INFORMATION

TYPICAL VALUES	Per 100g	Per Biscuit
Energy	2053kJ 490kcal	70kJ 17kcal
Protein	10.4g	0.4g
Carbohydrate	55.5g	[illegible].9g
(of which sugars)	3.5g	0.1g
Fat	25.2g	0.9g
(of which saturates)	15.3g	0.5g
Dietary Fibre	2.2g	0.1g
Sodium	1.0g	Trace

How do you get water in your diet?

Drinks are made almost completely of water. Most foods contain some water.

This means that you get some of the water you need from drinking and some from the food you eat. You need to drink about 15 cups of water every day.

d Make a list of all the drinks you have had today. How many cupfuls have you drunk so far?

QUESTIONS

Copy these sentences and fill in the spaces using the words below:

label nutrients water

Different foods contain different ________. Foods have a ________ to tell us which nutrients they contain. Food also contains some ________.

KEY POINTS

- Different foods contain different nutrients.
- Foods are labelled to tell us what nutrients they contain.
- Most foods contain some water.

A2 WHY IS FOOD IMPORTANT?

Why do you need nutrients?

Different nutrients do different jobs.

Look at the table. It tells you what different nutrients do in your body.

Nutrient	What's its job?
fat	store of energy
protein	growth
carbohydrate	quick source of energy
fibre	helps waste move through the gut

Carbohydrates and **fats** give you energy. They are both like a battery. They store energy.

Protein helps you grow and helps repair any damage to your body.

a **Which nutrient will help your body repair a cut on your finger?**

Vitamins are also important in food. You need only small amounts of them. Look at the table. It tells you what different vitamins do in your body.

These are both energy stores.

Vitamin	What's its job?
A	lets you see in the dark
B	keeps nerves healthy
C	keeps gums and skin healthy
D	keeps teeth and bones strong

Look at the picture. It shows what might happen to your gums if you do not eat any vitamin C.

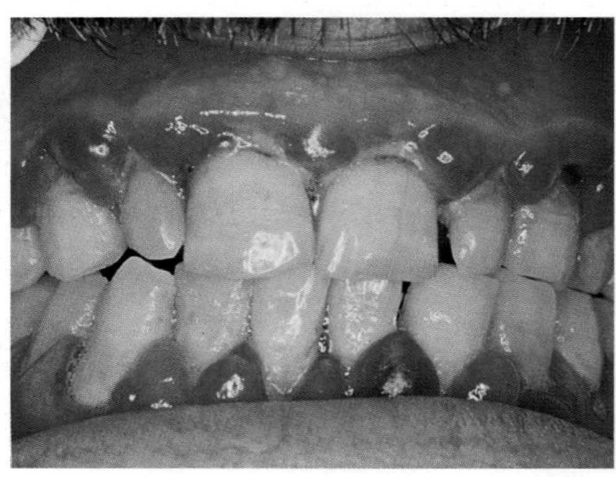

Minerals are also important in food. You only need small amounts. Look at the table. It tells you what different minerals do in your body.

Mineral	What's its job?
calcium	keeps teeth and bones strong
iron	helps the blood carry oxygen

b **Name one mineral and one vitamin that help to keep teeth and bones strong.**

Why do you need water?

You can live for 60 days without food. But you can only live for three days without water. Water has some important jobs to do in your body. You need water:

1. to get rid of poisonous waste, which leaves in your urine
2. to move things around your body in the blood
3. to make sweat, to keep you cool
4. for the chemical reactions that happen in your body.

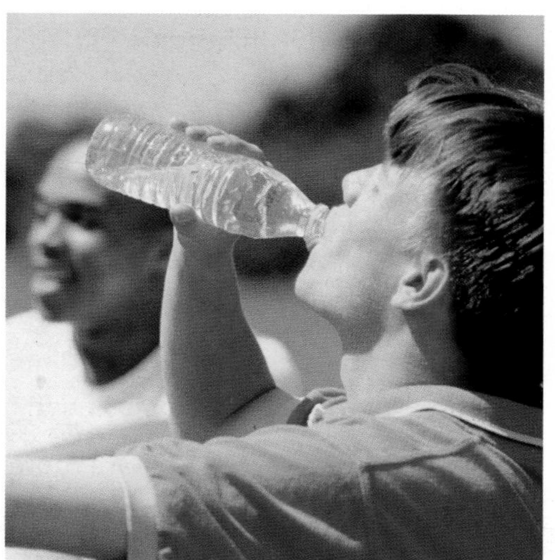

c **If you were lost in a desert without water, how long do you think you could survive?**

Why do you need fibre?

Fibre keeps waste moving through your digestive system. It gives your gut something to push against so you can get rid of the waste quickly.

QUESTIONS

1 Why do you need vitamin C in your food?

2 Why do you need protein in your food?

3 What jobs does water do in your body?

4 What job does fibre do in your body?

KEY POINTS

- Different nutrients do different jobs.
- You need water to keep you alive.
- Fibre helps your digestive system to get rid of waste quickly.

A3 A BALANCED DIET

What is a balanced diet?

Your **diet** is what you eat. A **balanced diet** provides the right amounts of energy and nutrients that you need to survive.

Balanced diets for everyone

A balanced diet is different for different people. Look at the table. It shows that different people need different things in their diet.

Size	The bigger you are, the more food you need.
Age	Young people tend to be very active. They are also growing very quickly. This means they need to eat more food.
Male or female?	Males need more fat and carbohydrate to give them energy. Females need more vitamins and minerals such as vitamin A and iron.
How active are you?	If you are more active and play lots of sport, you will need to eat more food. If you eat too much and are not active, you will get fat.

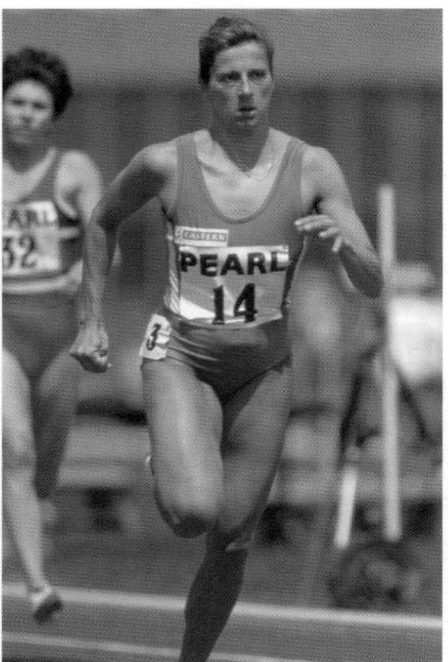

a **Look at the pictures. Why does the young woman running need more food than the man playing darts?**

Across the world, different people eat different foods. Some people do not eat meat because it is against their religion or their beliefs. They are called **vegetarians**.

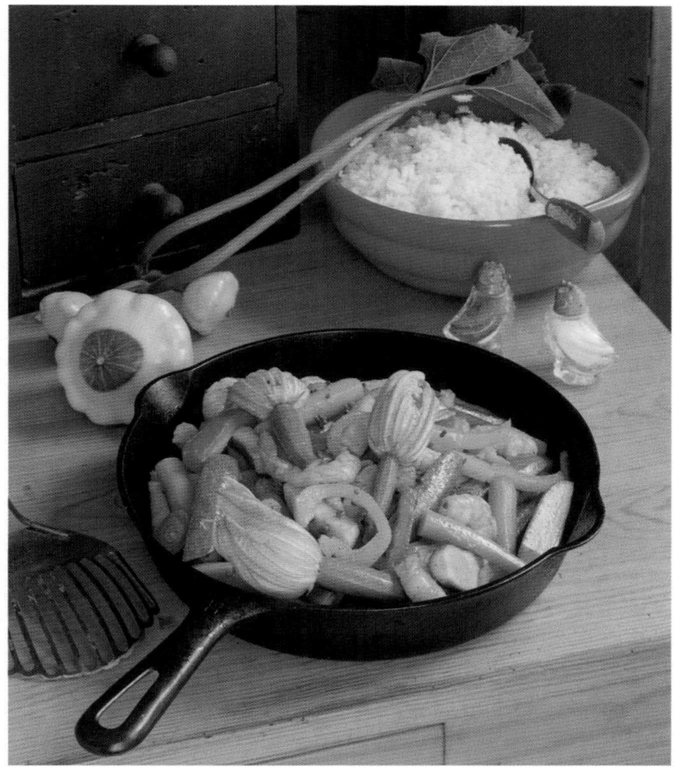

Why do some people have special diets?

Different people's bodies need different balanced diets.

- People with heart disease should eat very little fat.
- A pregnant woman needs extra protein and minerals for her growing baby.
- A mother who is breast-feeding needs extra fat to make milk for her baby.

(b) Give an example of one person who needs a special balanced diet.

QUESTIONS

Copy these sentences, choosing the correct words:

A balanced diet contains **some/all** of the nutrients that we need. A balanced diet is **different/the same** for different people.

KEY POINTS

- A balanced diet contains all the nutrients that we need.
- A balanced diet is different for different people.

HOW DO YOU CHOOSE WHAT TO EAT?

Can we believe in adverts?

We all know that we should eat a balanced diet. But how do we know what to eat each day?

Newspapers and magazines have articles and adverts telling us what we should eat. But can we believe them? They may be written by companies who want us to buy their food.

a **Why should we not always believe what we read in adverts?**

What does the media say?

Newspapers often have 'scare stories' about food. It helps them to sell more newspapers. It is often very difficult to know whether to believe them.

b **Why should we not always believe what we read in the newspapers?**

Exclusive: Millions of cans in Benzene contamination alert

FIZZY DRINKS HEALTH SCARE

DOUBLE ALERT ON EGG AND CHICKENS PERIL

APPLE JUICE IN CANCER SCARE

NOW FOOT AND MOUTH SPREADS TO HUMANS

What does research say?

We can also get information about diet from scientific research. The research is often only on one topic. This information comes from people like:

- The British Heart Foundation.

  They give information about what to eat for a healthy heart. But remember, you need to keep the rest of your body healthy too.

- The Potato Marketing Board.

  They tell you how good potatoes are for you. But remember, you should also eat other vegetables as part of your balanced diet.

C Will reading one piece of research give you complete advice for a balanced diet?

The best advice for a balanced diet

1. Don't eat too much of any nutrient.
   - If you have too much salt you can get high blood pressure.
   - Eating too much fat or carbohydrate can make you overweight.
2. Don't eat too little of any nutrient.
   - If you eat too little vitamin D, your bones and teeth will not stay healthy.
   - If you always eat low calorie food, your body will not get enough fat and carbohydrate to stay healthy.

QUESTIONS

Copy these sentences and fill in the spaces using the words below:

believe nutrient much

We should not ________ everything we see in the newspapers about food.

We should not eat too little or too ________ of any ________.

KEY POINTS

- Do not eat too much or too little of any nutrient.

A5 WHAT HAPPENS TO FOOD INSIDE THE DIGESTIVE SYSTEM?

What does the digestive system do?

When you eat food, it goes through a long tube. The tube goes from the **mouth**, through the body to the **anus**. The long tube is called the **digestive system**. Look at the picture.

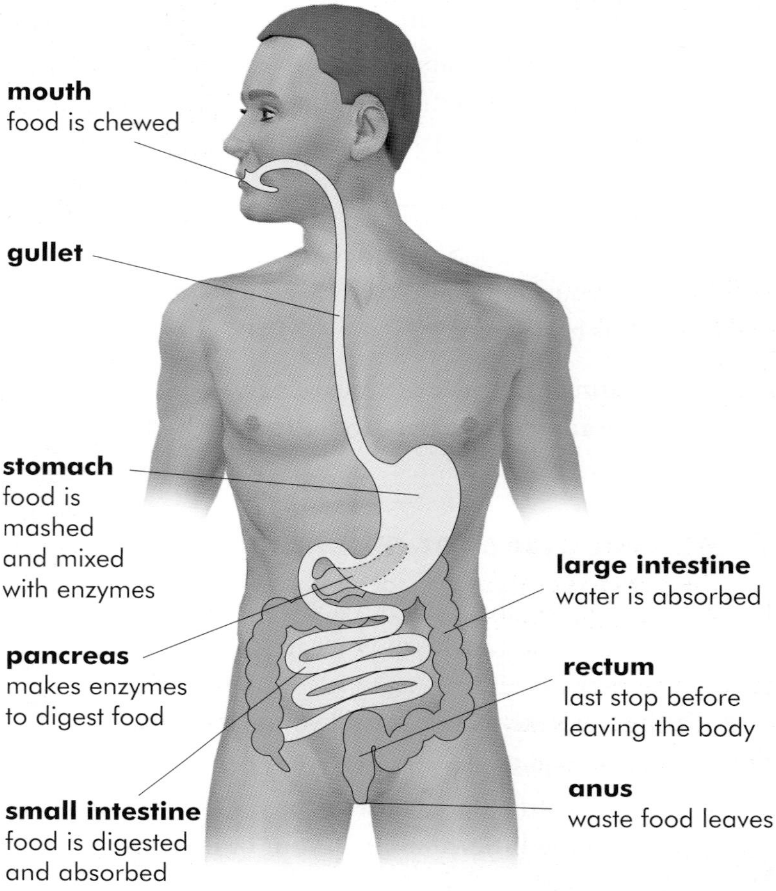

a **What does the stomach do?**

b **What does the large intestine do?**

mouth
food is chewed

gullet

stomach
food is mashed and mixed with enzymes

pancreas
makes enzymes to digest food

small intestine
food is digested and absorbed

large intestine
water is absorbed

rectum
last stop before leaving the body

anus
waste food leaves

What is digestion?

As food travels through the digestive system it is broken down in the small intestine. The nutrients are taken out of the food for your body to use. They are broken down into small particles. This is called **digestion**.

Nutrients need to pass through the walls of the small intestine into your body so your body can use them. The walls of the small intestine have very tiny holes that allow small nutrient particles to pass through. After digestion, the nutrients are small enough to pass through these holes in the walls of the small intestine.

c **Why do nutrients need to be broken down into small particles?**

What is absorption?

Jake is eating some rice. Rice contains a carbohydrate called **starch**. Starch particles are too big to pass through the holes in the walls of the small intestine.

Trying to get starch to pass through the tiny holes in the walls of the small intestine is like trying to get peas to go through a sieve.

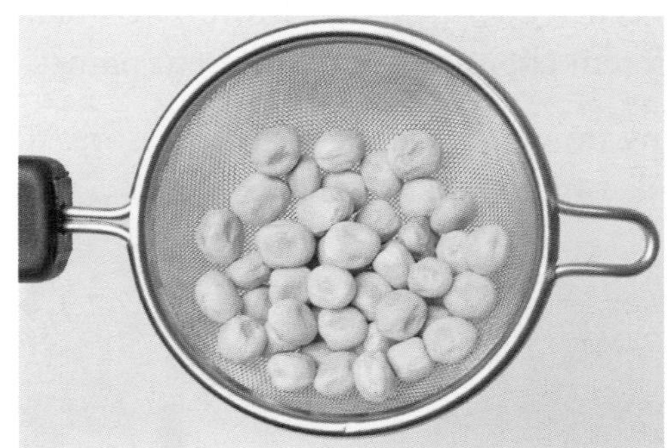

d **What would you need to do to the peas to get them to pass through the sieve?**

When the nutrients are small enough they can pass through the holes in the walls of the small intestine. This is called **absorption**.

QUESTIONS

Copy the crossword grid and complete it.

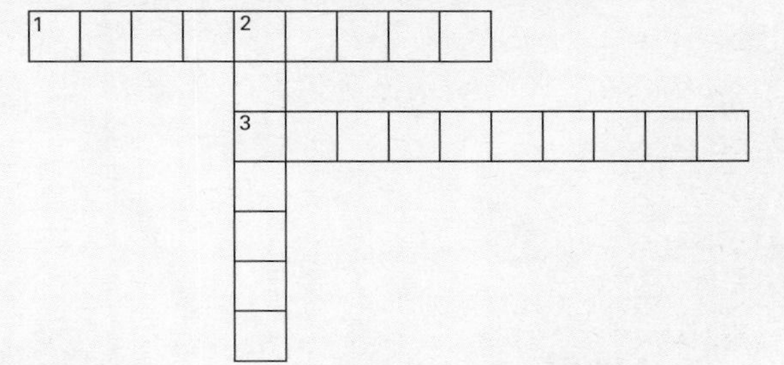

1 *across:* When nutrients are broken down into small particles.
2 *down:* After digestion, particles are **bigger/smaller**.
3 *across:* What happens when particles pass through the holes in the small intestine wall.

KEY POINTS

- The digestive system is a tube going from the mouth to the anus.
- Digestion means breaking down the nutrients into small particles.
- Absorption happens when the small particles of nutrients pass through tiny holes in the walls of the small intestine.

A6 WHAT DO DIGESTIVE ENZYMES DO?

How does digestion happen?

Chewing breaks down food into smaller pieces. This is called **mechanical digestion**. But the pieces of food are still too big to pass through the holes in the walls of the small intestine. They can't be absorbed.

To break down the food into smaller particles, you need **enzymes.** Enzymes are chemicals which work like very tiny scissors. They chop up the food into smaller particles. This is called **chemical digestion**. The smaller particles are different chemicals with different names.

It is like chopping up words with a pair of scissors. You end up with a pile of letters, not words.

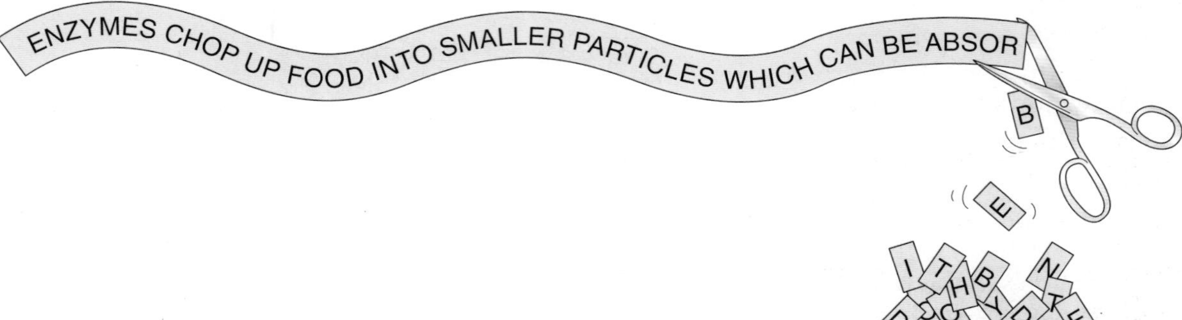

ENZYMES CHOP UP FOOD INTO SMALLER PARTICLES WHICH CAN BE ABSOR
B
E

What do enzymes do?

One example of an enzyme is **amylase.** You have amylase in the saliva in your mouth.

Try this! When you get home tonight, chew a piece of bread but do not swallow it. Keep it in your mouth for at least ten minutes.

The enzymes in your saliva will break down the starch into sugar.

a **Why does the bread start to taste sweet after about ten minutes?**

Sugar particles are much smaller than starch. We can say that the enzyme has digested the starch.

Look at the picture opposite. It shows how the enzyme amylase breaks down starch into sugar.

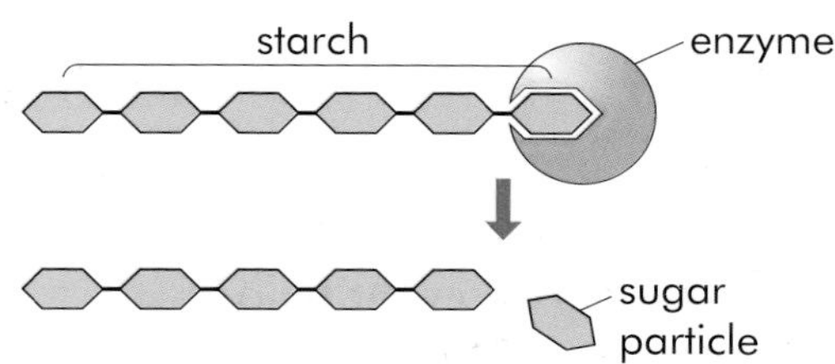

Sugar particles are so small that they can pass through the holes in the walls of the small intestine. Look at the picture below. It shows how the sugar particles can pass through the holes in the walls of the small intestine.

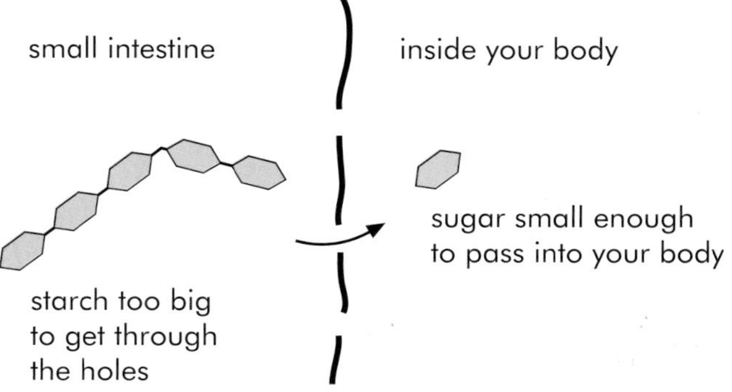

What affects how enzymes work?

Enzymes work best in particular conditions.

- All the enzymes in your body work best at **body temperature**. This is 37 °C.
- Enzymes in your stomach prefer **acidic** conditions.
- Enzymes in your small intestine prefer **alkaline** conditions.

**(b) Your mouth is slightly alkaline.
Why will amylase not work properly in your stomach?**

QUESTIONS

Copy these sentences and fill in the spaces using the words below:

small intestine 37 smaller

Enzymes break down food into ________ particles so that they can be absorbed through the walls of the ________ . Enzymes in your body work best at a temperature of ________ °C.

KEY POINTS

- Enzymes break food up into smaller particles.
- Enzymes work best in particular conditions.

A7 WHERE ARE THE PRODUCTS OF DIGESTION USED?

How are nutrients transported around the body?

Nutrients from digestion are absorbed into the body. They pass out of the small intestine through the tiny holes and go into your **blood**.

Your blood is a bit like a postal service. It carries nutrients from the digestive system and delivers them to all the cells of your body. Look at the picture. It shows blood flowing to the cells of the body.

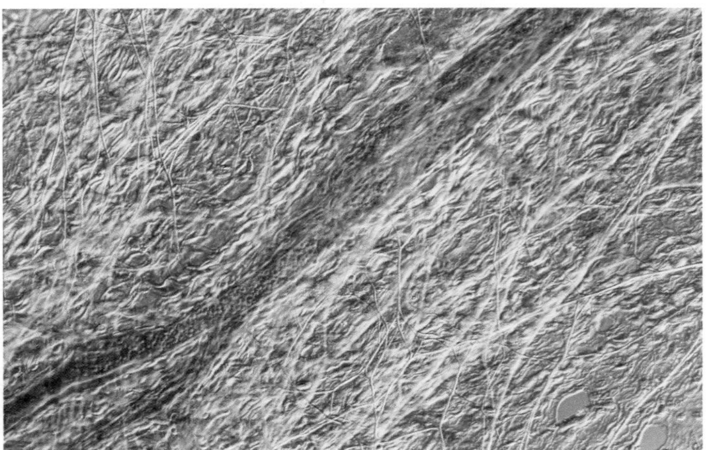

How are nutrients used?

Remember, each nutrient is needed by the body for a different job.

- Protein is needed for growth and repair to your body.
- Carbohydrates like sugar are needed for energy.

What happens to food that cannot be digested?

A part of our food, called **fibre**, cannot be digested. This is because you do not have an enzyme to digest fibre. Fruit and vegetables contain lots of fibre.

Grass is made almost completely of fibre. Animals that eat grass, like cows and sheep, have an enzyme to digest the fibre.

a **Why do humans not eat grass?**

Look at the picture. All of these foods contain some fibre.

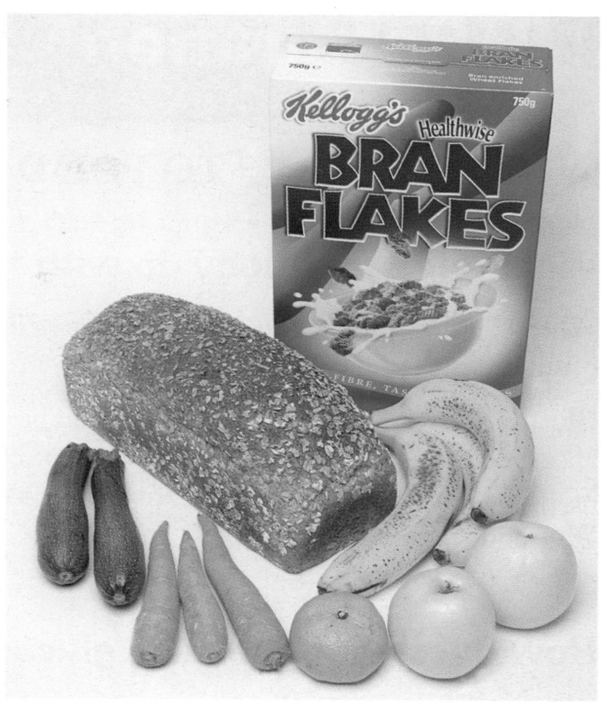

b **Make a list of foods in the picture that contain fibre.**

You cannot digest fibre, so it just passes straight through your digestive system. Because we do not absorb fibre, most people do not think it is a nutrient. But it is very important to eat some fibre every day. It helps to keep the food moving through your digestive system.

Fibre keeps the food moving in two ways.

1. Fibre absorbs water. This keeps the food in your intestine wet. Imagine what would happen if the food in your intestine dried out. It might get stuck half way down.
2. Food moves through your gut because muscles push it along. Fibre gives the muscles something to push against.

What happens to water?

Water in your large intestine is absorbed back into your body and into the blood. If there is too much water in your blood, then your body gets rid of it in the urine.

QUESTIONS

Copy these sentences and fill in the spaces using the words below:

carbohydrates   blood   fibre

The ________ transports nutrients around the body. ________ cannot be digested. Proteins are used for growth. ________ give you energy.

KEY POINTS

- The blood transports nutrients to all the cells in the body.
- Protein is used for growth. Carbohydrates are used for energy.
- Fibre in food cannot be digested.

B Respiration

B1 WHAT HAPPENS TO FOOD AFTER DIGESTION?

What does your body do with food?

When you digest food, one of the substances that is produced is a sugar called **glucose**.

Glucose particles are so small that they can be absorbed through the small intestine and into the blood. The blood carries glucose around your body. Your body uses the glucose to get energy.

How does your body use glucose?

Glucose is in many types of food. Look at the picture. The rugby player is drinking a high-energy drink containing glucose.

a **Why do rugby players use high-energy drinks?**

The blood takes the glucose to the cells of your body.

Some cells such as muscle cells work harder than other cells. This means they need more energy, so they use more glucose.

How do cells get energy from glucose?

When we want to release the energy from fuel, we burn it. We burn coal on the fire to release heat energy.

We can show what happens by using a word equation.

fuel + oxygen → carbon dioxide + water + energy

We can also burn food to release energy. Look at the picture. It shows a biscuit being burnt to release heat energy.

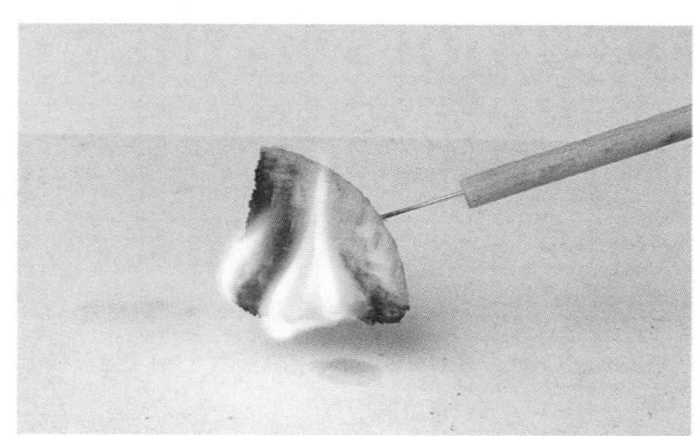

b What type of energy is released when we burn food?

Your body can also release the energy from the glucose in food. It happens in every cell of your body. The process is called **aerobic respiration**. The energy is released much more slowly. This is just as well – otherwise we would burst into flames every time we ate any food.

We can show that we release heat energy from glucose by taking our **body temperature**. We all have a body temperature of about 37 °C. Room temperature is about 20 °C. We are much warmer than the room because of the heat energy being released by the aerobic respiration of our food.

c Why is your body temperature warmer than the room?

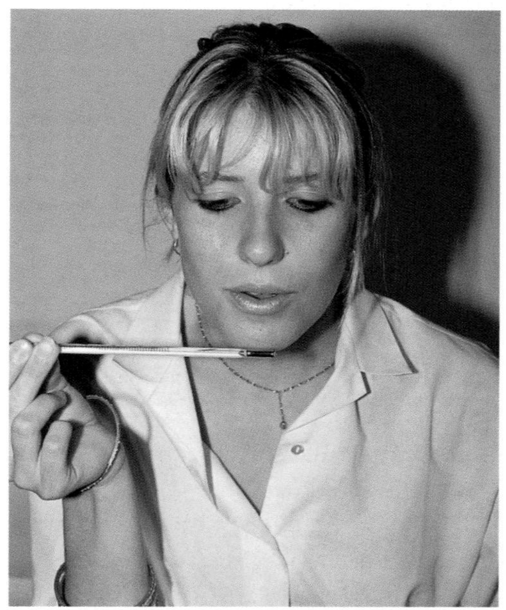

Breathing on a thermometer makes the temperature rise.

What else does aerobic respiration produce?

Look again at the equation for burning at the bottom of the page opposite. Carbon dioxide and water are produced. The cells in your body also produce carbon dioxide and water when they respire.

QUESTIONS

Copy these sentences and fill in the spaces using the words below:

water dioxide glucose respiration

Your body gets its energy from ________.
We call the process aerobic ________ .
It also produces carbon ________ and ________ .

KEY POINTS

- Your body breaks down some food into glucose.
- Glucose provides your body with energy.
- Energy is released from the glucose by the process of aerobic respiration.

HOW DOES OXYGEN GET INTO THE BLOOD?

What happens in your lungs?

Your cells need oxygen for aerobic respiration. When you breathe in, oxygen passes from your lungs into your blood. The blood then carries the oxygen to all the cells of your body.

a What does the blood carry to all the cells of your body?

When your cells respire, they produce carbon dioxide. Your blood carries the carbon dioxide to your lungs. When you breathe out you get rid of this carbon dioxide.

Look at the table.

Gas	Air breathed in	Air breathed out
oxygen	21%	16%
carbon dioxide	0.03%	4%

b Which gas does your body use from the air you breathe in?

How do you absorb oxygen?

When you breathe in, air goes down a tube called the **trachea**, into your chest. The trachea divides like branches on a tree. Each tube gets smaller and smaller. The tubes end in small sacs called **alveoli** (one is called an alveolus). Look at the picture.

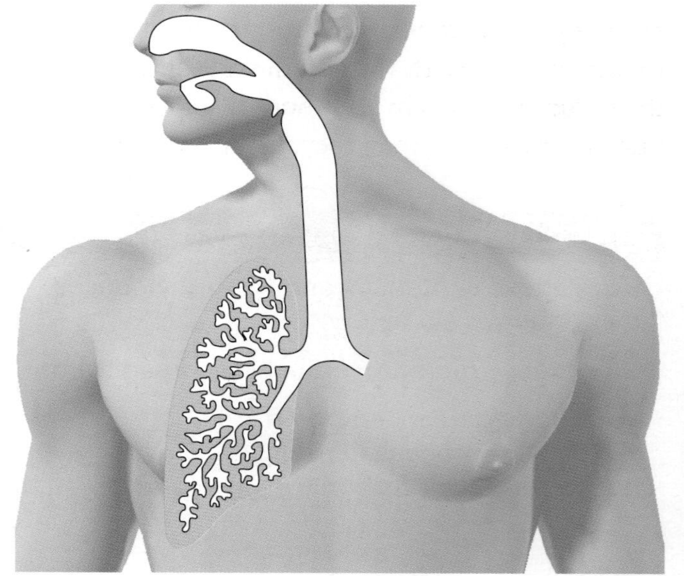

c Copy the picture and draw an arrow going from the nose down to the alveoli.

When the air you breathe in gets into the alveoli, the oxygen passes into the blood. Carbon dioxide from respiration passes from the blood into the alveoli. Then you breathe it out.

The gases move in and out of the blood. This is called **gas exchange**. It can happen because each alveolus is surrounded by tiny blood vessels.

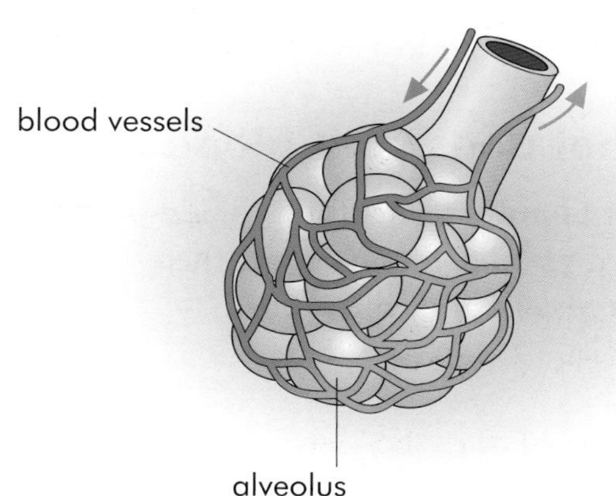

Why are the alveoli good at their job?

- **There are lots of them.** If we could take them out and flatten them, they would easily cover a tennis court.
- **They have very thin walls.** This lets the oxygen and carbon dioxide pass through very easily.
- **There are lots of blood vessels.** This helps to bring the carbon dioxide to the lungs and carry away the oxygen.

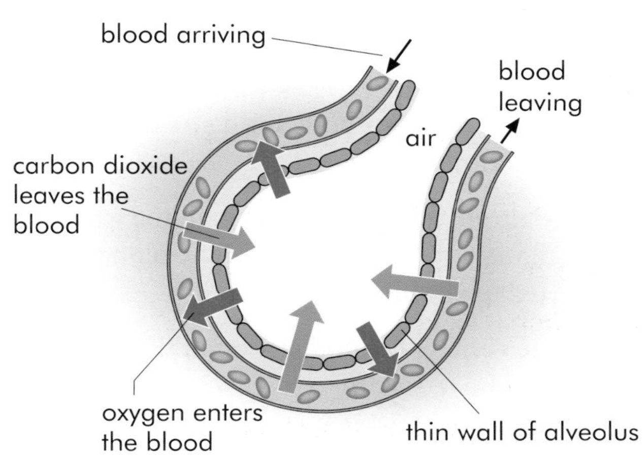

An alveolus in the lung

Smoking damages your lungs

Smoking makes the alveoli burst so there are fewer of them. This means the lungs can take less oxygen into the blood. Smokers have to breathe faster to get the same amount of oxygen as a healthy person.

QUESTIONS

Copy these sentences and fill in the spaces using the words below:

alveoli carbon dioxide oxygen

Your lungs absorb ________ from the air and breathe out ________ from the blood. The oxygen is absorbed through small sacs called ________ .

KEY POINTS

- The lungs contain lots of small sacs called alveoli.
- In the alveoli, oxygen passes into the blood.
- In the alveoli, carbon dioxide passes out of the blood.

B3 HOW DO OXYGEN AND GLUCOSE REACH CELLS?

What does your blood do?

Your **blood** is made from a liquid called **plasma**. In the plasma there are **red cells** and **white cells**.

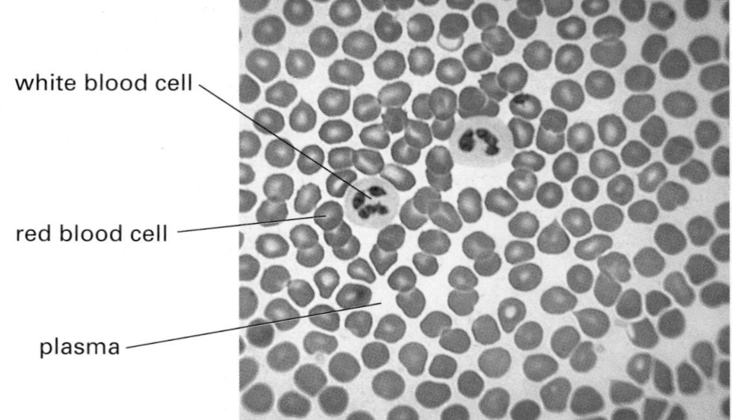

Before respiration

Cells all around your body need glucose and oxygen for respiration.

- Glucose enters the body through the walls of the small intestine. It dissolves in the blood and is carried to all the cells of the body.
- Oxygen enters the body through the lungs. The red blood cells carry the oxygen. They take the oxygen to all the cells of the body.

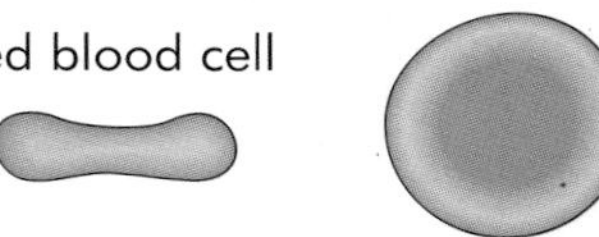

a **What part of the blood carries the oxygen round the body?**

After respiration

The cells need to get rid of carbon dioxide and water after respiration.

- The blood carries the carbon dioxide. It takes the carbon dioxide to the lungs. Then you breathe out to get rid of the carbon dioxide.
- Water is also produced by respiration. The blood carries the water to the kidneys. The kidneys get rid of the water by making urine.

b **What does the blood carry to the lungs?**

What happens when blood reaches your cells?

The blood is pumped around your body by your heart. The blood travels through tubes called **blood vessels**. There are millions of very tiny blood vessels. These are called **capillaries**.

Capillaries are very thin. This makes it easy for glucose and oxygen to pass through from the blood to the cells in the body. It also makes it easy for carbon dioxide and water to pass from the cells of the body into the blood.

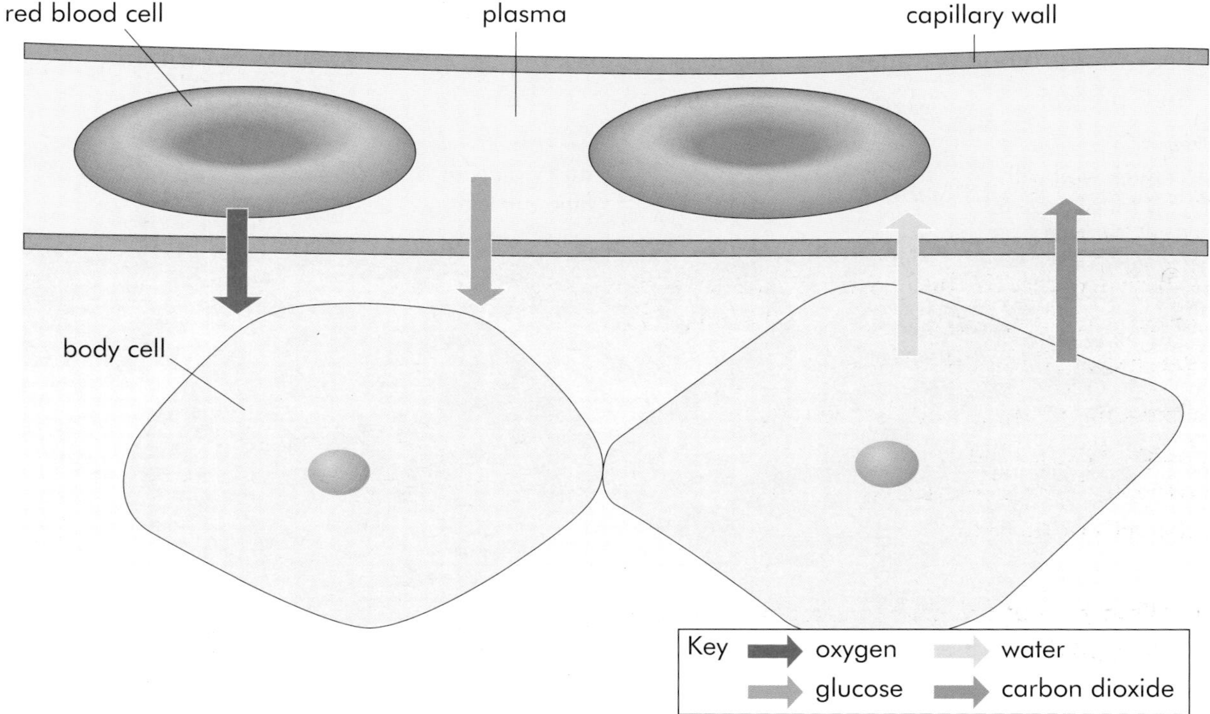

QUESTIONS

Copy these sentences, choosing the correct words:

Oxygen is carried from the **small intestine/ lungs** by **red blood cells/plasma**.

Carbon dioxide and water are carried from the cells to the **small intestine/lungs** by the **white blood cells/plasma**.

KEY POINTS

- Blood carries glucose from the small intestine to the cells.
- Red blood cells carry oxygen from the lungs to the cells.
- Blood carries carbon dioxide from the cells to the lungs.

B4 HOW DOES THE HEART PUMP BLOOD AROUND THE BODY?

How does the heart work?

Your **heart** pumps blood around your body. It pumps the blood through tiny tubes called **blood vessels**. There are three types of blood vessel.

- **Arteries** carry blood away from the heart. They have thick muscular walls because the blood is under high pressure.
- **Veins** carry blood back to the heart. They have much thinner walls because the blood is not under pressure.
- **Capillaries** carry blood between the arteries and the veins. They are too small to see with the naked eye.

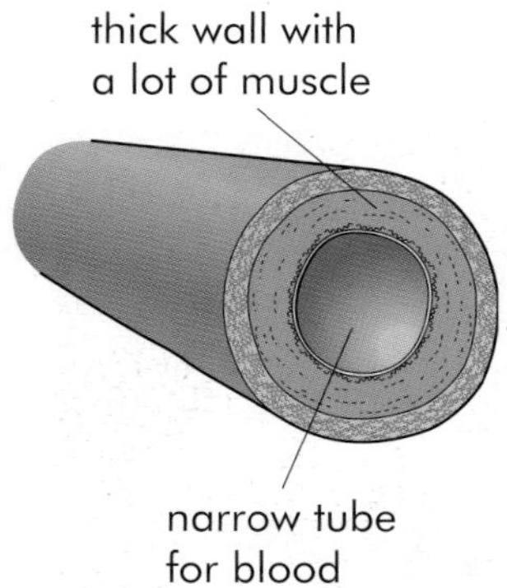

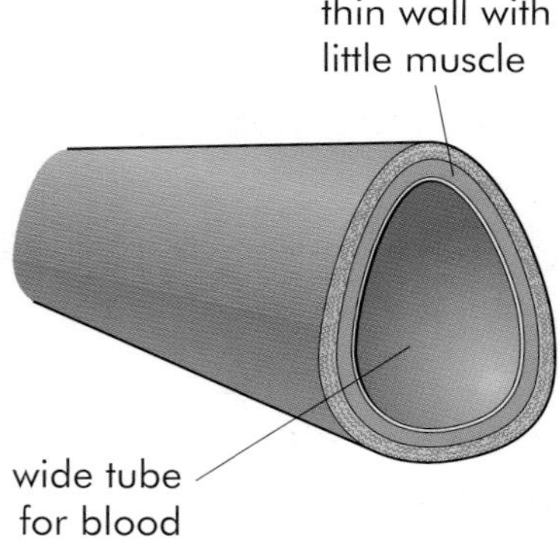

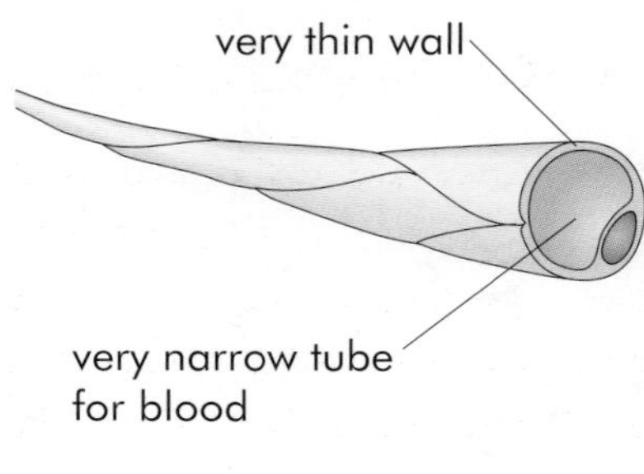

The picture opposite shows how the heart pumps blood through these blood vessels.

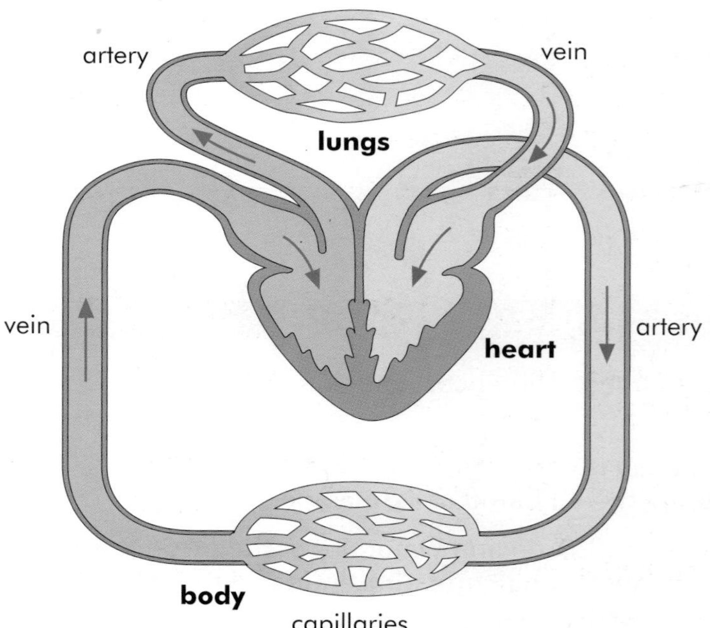

Look at the last picture again.

a **Which kind of blood vessel carries blood from arteries to veins?**

b **Put your finger on a vein in the picture. Follow the arrows round until you get back to your starting point. How many times did you go through the heart?**

The blood flows through the heart twice because the heart is really two pumps joined together. One pump would not be enough to pump the blood all the way round the body.

What happens when the blood cannot supply enough oxygen?

When you exercise, you need more energy. Your heart beats faster to supply more blood carrying oxygen to the cells.

c **What happens to your heartbeat when you exercise?**

If you exercise really hard, your heart cannot beat fast enough to supply all the oxygen your cells need. Your body has a clever trick. For a short time it can release the energy from glucose without using oxygen. Your body can break the glucose down into **lactic acid** and release energy. This is called **anaerobic respiration**.

But lactic acid makes your muscles ache and stops you running. After you stop you have to carry on panting to breathe in lots of oxygen. The oxygen lets your body break down the lactic acid. This is why you are still out of breath even when you stop running.

d **Name the kind of respiration that releases energy without oxygen.**

QUESTIONS

Copy these sentences and fill in the spaces using the words below:

arteries blood capillaries veins

Your heart pumps ________ around the body. ________ take blood from the heart and ________ return blood to it. Arteries and veins are joined by ________.

KEY POINTS

- Your heart pumps blood around your body through arteries, veins and capillaries.
- The blood carries oxygen and glucose to your cells.

B5 WHO SOLVED THE MYSTERY OF BLOOD CIRCULATION?

What did Galen find out about circulation?

Galen was a Greek doctor. He lived about 700 years ago. He spent a lot of his life treating Roman emperors. Galen had the following ideas about blood.

Galen's ideas

ⓐ **Look at the picture. Only one of Galen's ideas was correct. Which do you think it was?**

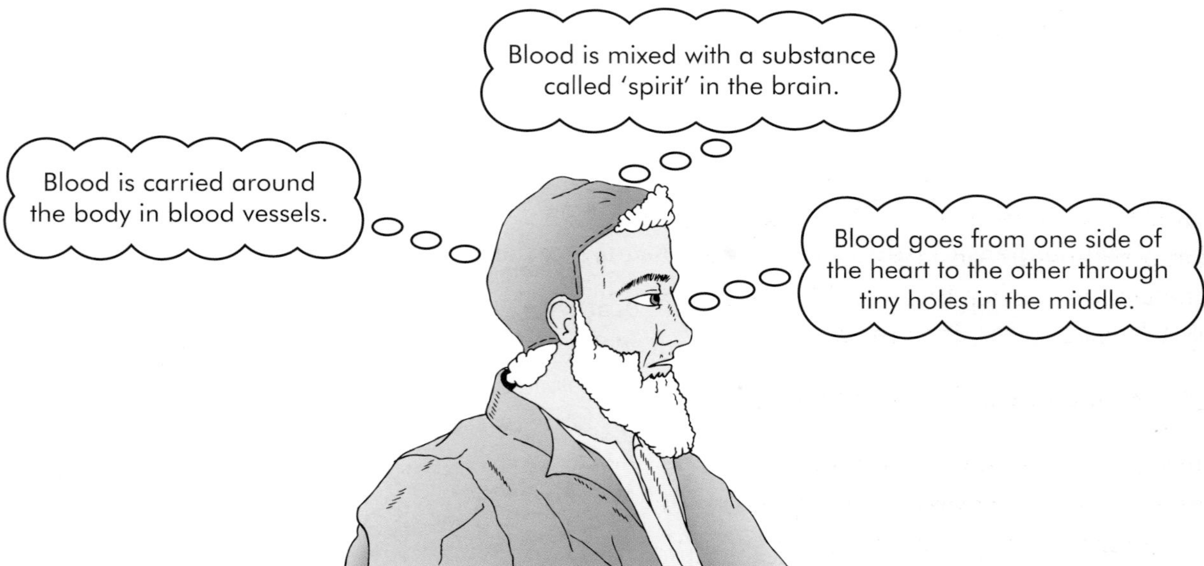

Blood is mixed with a substance called 'spirit' in the brain.
Blood is carried around the body in blood vessels.
Blood goes from one side of the heart to the other through tiny holes in the middle.

What did Harvey find out about circulation?

William Harvey was a doctor. He lived about 400 years ago. He worked out exactly how blood travels around the body.

- Harvey looked carefully at the heart. He realised that it was a pump that pumped blood around the body.
- Harvey measured how much blood the heart pumped with every beat. He then worked out how much blood the heart pumped every hour.

He realised that the heart pumped so much blood that the body could not hold it all. It must be pumping a smaller amount around the body, over and over again. This is called the blood **circulation**.

ⓑ **What job did Harvey discover the heart does?**

- Harvey looked at the blood vessels. He saw that some of them had valves. He tried to push liquids the wrong way through these vessels and realised that blood only flows in one direction.

Look at the picture. It shows how Harvey worked out the position of the valves in the arm.

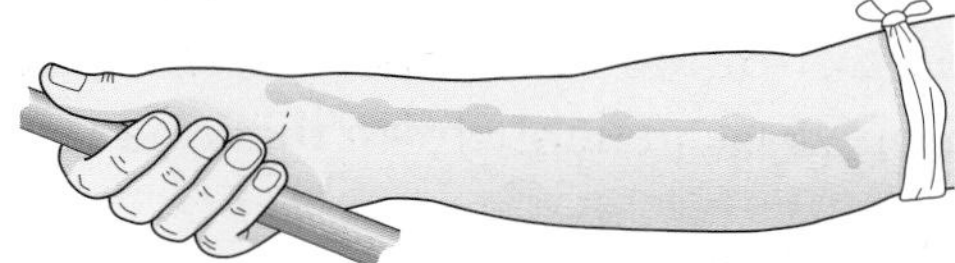

Swellings show the position of the valves.

Warning!
Harvey's experiment is dangerous and should only be done with your teacher.

c What job do the valves do?

Harvey still had a problem

Unfortunately, William Harvey did not have the complete answer. He could see that the arteries got smaller and smaller. But he could not see the tiny blood vessels that joined the arteries to the veins.

d What do we call these tiny blood vessels?

Although he could not see them, Harvey predicted that these tiny blood vessels, called capillaries, existed. Many years later when microscopes were invented, people could see these tiny blood vessels for the first time.

e Why could Harvey not see the tiny blood capillaries?

QUESTIONS

Copy these sentences and fill in the spaces using the words below:

circulated Galen Harvey

A Greek doctor called ________ realised that blood was carried in blood vessels. About 300 years later, another doctor called ________ realised that blood ________ around the body.

KEY POINTS

- Galen thought that blood was carried in blood vessels.
- William Harvey worked out how the blood circulated around the body.

B6 DO OTHER LIVING THINGS RESPIRE?

Do other animals respire?

We saw in Topic B1 that humans respire to release energy from their food. Other animals also need to respire to get energy from the food that they eat.

You release heat energy when you respire. That is why your body is always warmer than the room.

Animals release heat energy

Look at the picture. Read the two different temperatures.

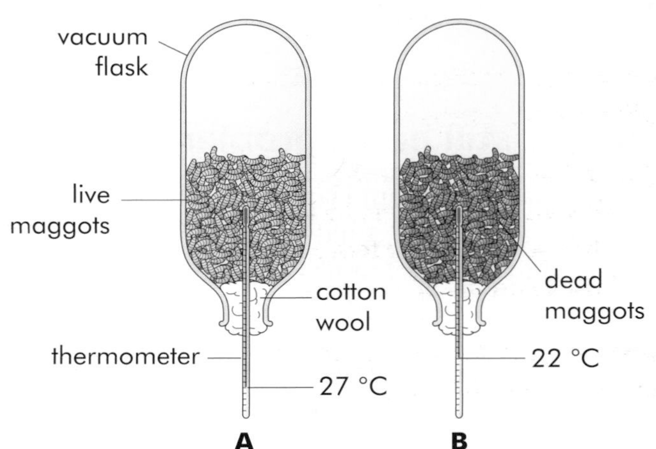

a What difference do you notice between the temperature of the live maggots and the temperature of the dead maggots?

Just like humans, maggots release heat energy when they respire.

Animals produce carbon dioxide

Look at the picture opposite. When Julia breathes out through the straw and into the limewater, it goes cloudy.

b What does this tell us about Julia's breath?

Look at the picture of the mouse below. The air that the mouse breathes out turns limewater cloudy.

c What do the mouse and Julia have in common?

Animals respire just like humans. They use up oxygen to release energy from glucose, and they produce carbon dioxide and water.

Do plants respire too?

Plants respire just like animals. They use up oxygen to release energy from glucose, and they produce carbon dioxide and water.

Plants release heat energy

Look at the picture. Read the two different temperatures.

d What difference do you notice between the temperature of the live peas and the temperature of the dead peas?

Just like animals, peas release heat energy when they respire.

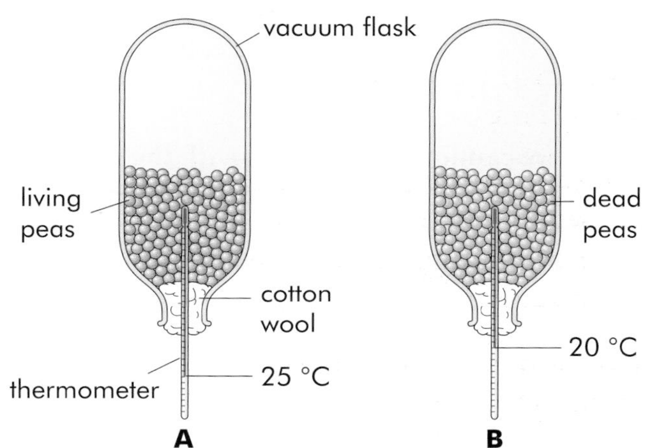

Plants produce carbon dioxide

Just like animals, plants release carbon dioxide when they respire.

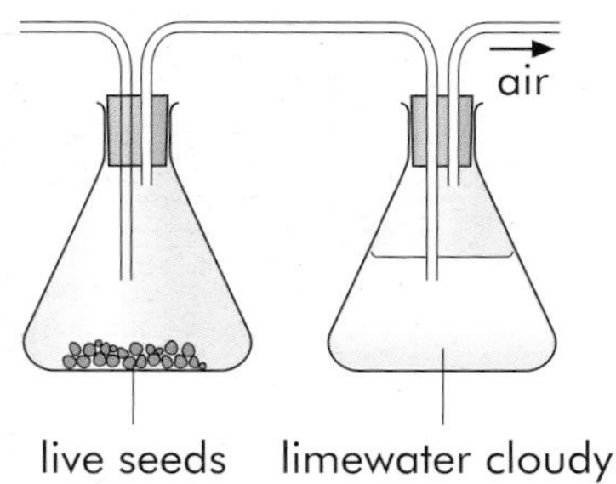

QUESTIONS

Copy these sentences, choosing the correct words:

Animals **respire/do not respire** just like humans. Plants **respire/do not respire** just like animals.

KEY POINTS

- Animals and plants respire, just like humans.

C Microbes and disease

C1 WHAT ARE MICROORGANISMS?

What do microorganisms do?

Microorganisms are often called **microbes**. They are living things that are so small that you need a microscope to see them. We can only see them with the naked eye when there are a lot of them together.

Look at the picture. It shows microbes called fungi growing on food.

a **If we cannot see microbes with the naked eye, why can we see the fungi growing on the food?**

Microbes are like other living things.

- They need food to use for respiration to get energy.
- They grow.
- They reproduce.

Some microbes are harmful. We use chemicals to kill them.

This photo shows some chemicals that kill microbes.

Some microbes are useful. We use them to make wine, bread and yoghurt.

What do microbes look like?

	Viruses	Bacteria	Fungi
What they look like	protein coat; genetic information	cell wall; cell membrane; cytoplasm; genetic information (not a nucleus)	pin-mould; mushroom
Size	**viruses** are tiny – over one million of them would fit on the point of a pin	**bacteria** are about 1000 times larger than viruses, but smaller than your cells	different **fungi** are different sizes
Structure	just a bag of chemical instructions used when the virus invades a cell	more like a normal cell, but they don't have a nucleus	lots of cells with nuclei, joined together
How harmful ones can make you ill	viruses invade your cells, which make copies of the viruses and then die – the viruses release poisons	bacteria multiply quickly and release poisons that make you ill	fungi grow quickly and release poisons that attack your cells
Uses	none	used to make yoghurt	make medicines called antibiotics, and are also used to make bread, wine and beer

b **Which is the smallest type of microbe?**

c **What useful things can microbes do?**

QUESTIONS

Copy these sentences and fill in the spaces using the words below:

ill   fungi   viruses

The smallest microbes are called ________ . Some microbes can make us ________, but we use others such as some ________ to make medicines.

KEY POINTS

- Microbes are very small.
- Some microbes cause disease, but others can be very useful.

C2 HOW CAN WE USE MICROBES?

Using microbes to make food

Bread

Yeast is a fungus. To make bread, we mix yeast with flour, warm water and sugar. The yeast feeds on the sugar and starts to grow.

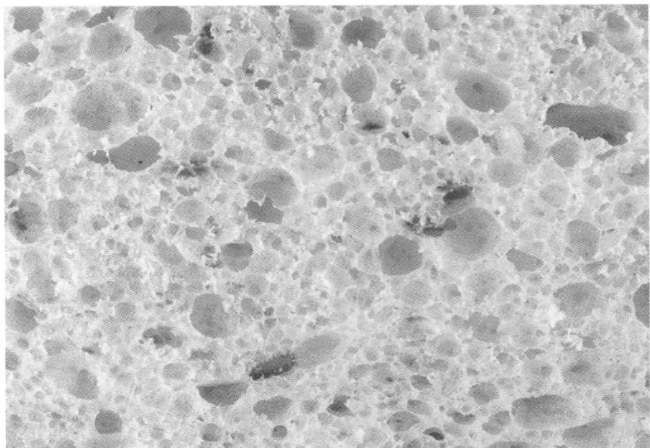

You know that all living things respire and give off carbon dioxide. When yeast respires it also gives off carbon dioxide. Because the yeast is mixed in with the flour, the gas cannot escape. Instead, bubbles of carbon dioxide form in the mixture. These make the mixture rise and expand. We bake the mixture in the oven to make bread.

Look at the picture. You can still see the bubbles of gas in the baked bread.

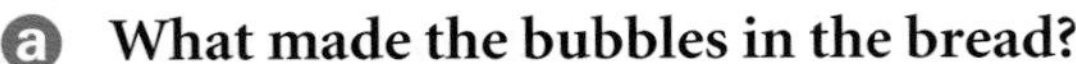

a What made the bubbles in the bread?

Yoghurt

Some bacteria can change milk into yoghurt. Milk contains a sugar called lactose. The bacteria turn the lactose into lactic acid. This is called **fermentation.** The lactic acid gives the yoghurt a sharp acidic taste.

b Why does yoghurt have a sharp taste?

The acid makes the protein in the milk stick together. This is why yoghurt is thick and creamy.

c Why is yoghurt thick and creamy?

How do we grow microbes in the lab?

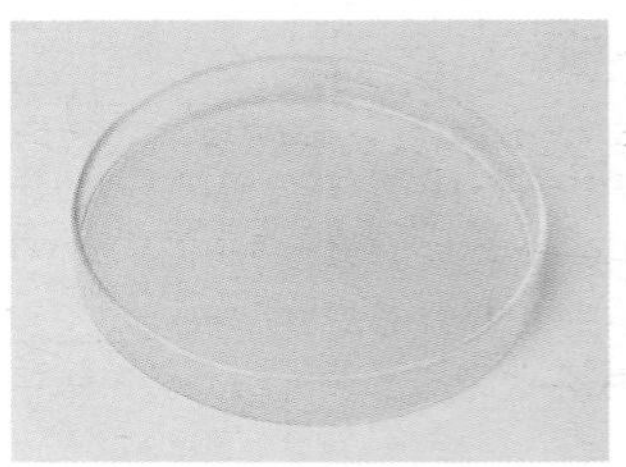

We grow microbes in the lab in a **Petri dish.** The Petri dish in the picture has a layer of **agar jelly** in it. The jelly contains all the food the microbes need to grow.

Imagine you are a doctor. A patient has food poisoning. Food poisoning is caused by microbes.

The patient says she ate some old fish paste yesterday. Perhaps the fish paste contains microbes that caused the food poisoning. To find out which microbe was to blame, you need to grow it until you have enough to recognise it.

1. Sterilise a wire loop by putting it in a hot Bunsen burner flame. This kills any other microbes.
2. Let the loop cool. Then dip it in the fish paste.

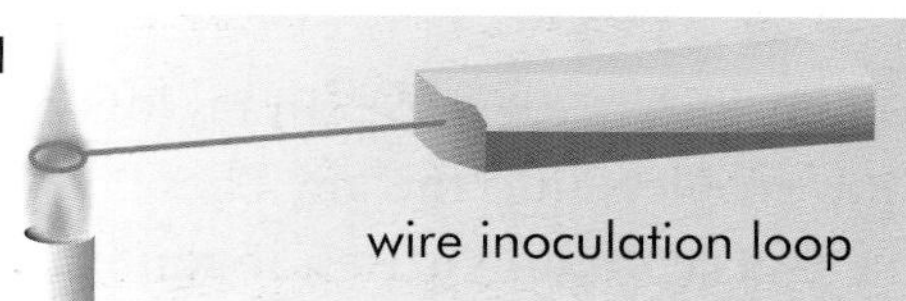

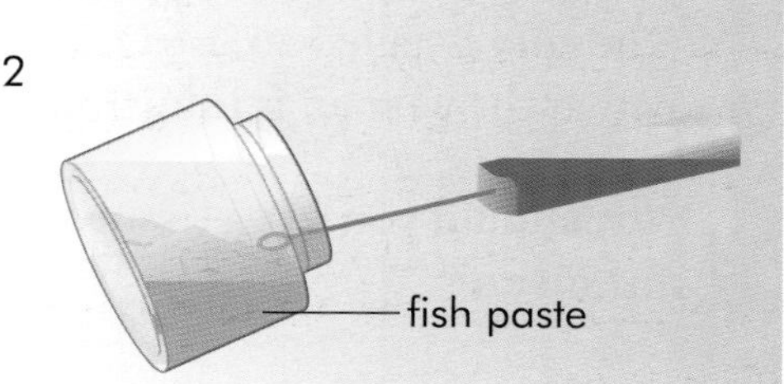

3. Remove the Petri dish lid and spread the fish paste on the agar.

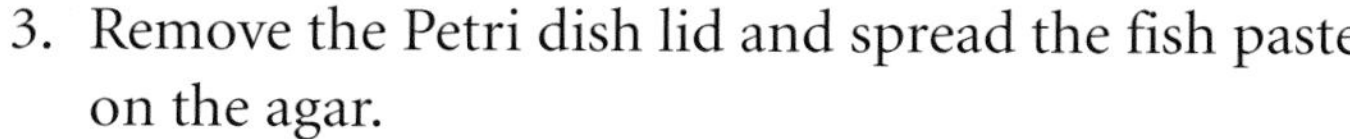

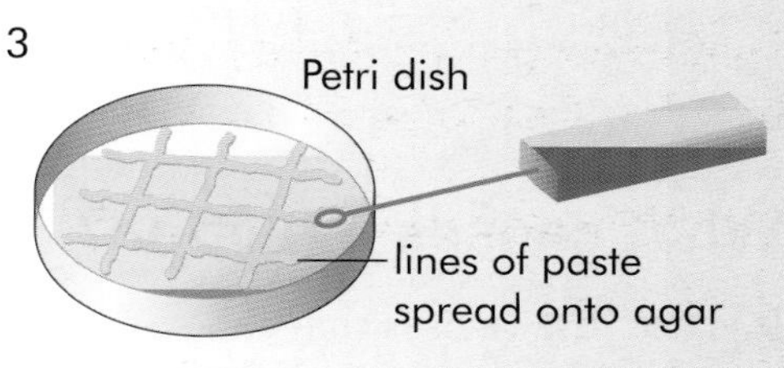

4. Replace the lid.
5. Tape the lid on the Petri dish. Remember: these microbes are dangerous. They cause food poisoning.
6. Leave the Petri dish upside down in a warm place for the microbes to grow.

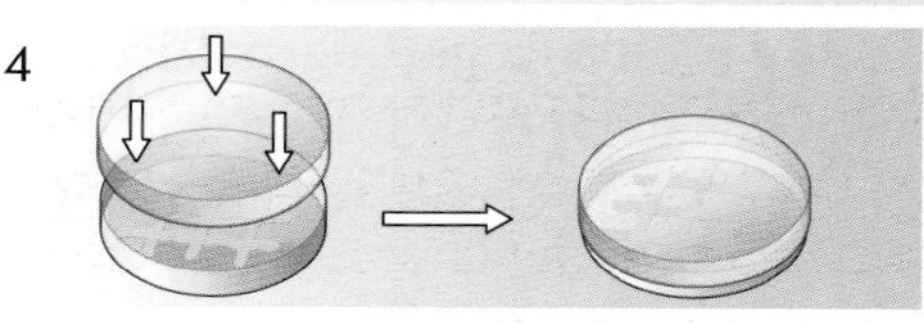

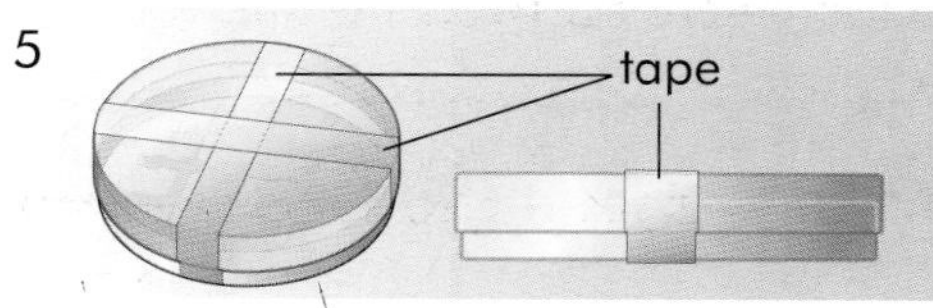

d Why should you never take the lid off the Petri dish to look at the microbes?

QUESTIONS

Copy these sentences and fill in the spaces using the words below:

agar bacteria Petri yeast

We use ________ to make bread. We use some ________ to make yoghurt. We can grow microbes on ________ jelly in a ________ dish.

KEY POINTS

- We use yeast to make bread. We use some bacteria to make yoghurt.
- We can grow microbes in a Petri dish in the lab.

C3 CAN MICROBES BE HARMFUL?

What is infection?

Look at the picture. The woman has a cold. Colds are caused by viruses.

When she sneezes, she sprays lots of tiny droplets into the air. These droplets contain viruses. If you breathe in any droplets, you may also catch a cold. The cold is called an **infection**. We say that the woman is **infectious**.

a Why should you use a tissue when you sneeze?

What causes infection?

It is not just viruses that can make us ill. Bacteria and fungi can also cause disease. A microbe that causes disease is called a **pathogen**. Viruses, bacteria and fungi are all types of microbes. Look at the table to see which microbes cause which diseases.

Viruses	Bacteria	Fungi
colds	meningitis	athlete's foot
flu	food poisoning	thrush
measles	TB	
chicken pox	typhoid	
AIDS	whooping cough	
	tetanus	

b Which kind of microbe causes measles?

c Which kind of microbe causes food poisoning?

How can microbes enter your body?

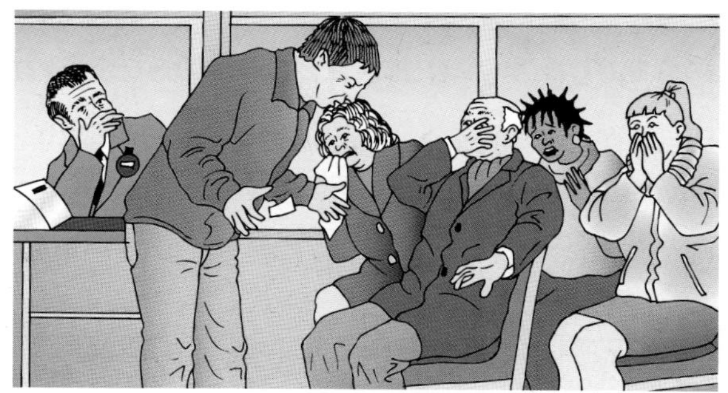

For infection to happen, a microbe must pass from one person to another. When this happens we say the microbe has been **transmitted**.

Microbes can be transmitted by:

- sneezing and someone breathing in the droplets
- eating infected food or drinking unclean water
- breathing in air containing microbes
- microbes getting into your blood through cuts and grazes
- during sexual intercourse. These microbes cause **sexually transmitted diseases**. An example is AIDS.
- microbes passing from a pregnant woman's blood across the placenta into her baby. This can happen with the virus that causes rubella (German measles). The virus can seriously damage the developing baby.

  The picture opposite shows how rubella can be transmitted.

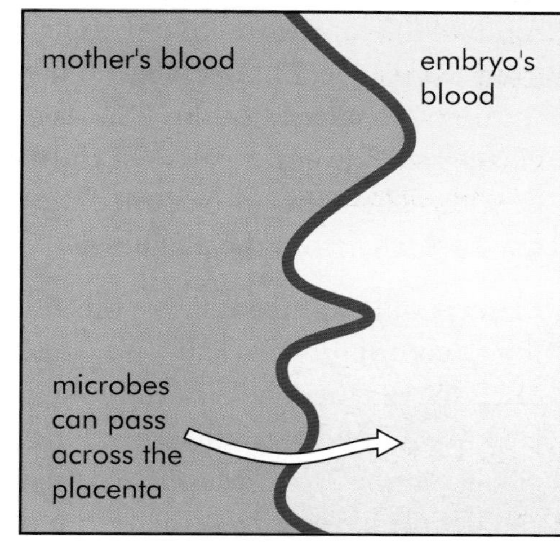

d **Write down five ways that microbes can be transmitted.**

How can we avoid infection?

- Cook food well – it kills the microbes.
- Wash your hands after going to the toilet.
- Drink only water that is clean.
- Don't share drinks.
- Clean and cover any cuts and grazes.
- Always use a condom during sexual intercourse.

QUESTIONS

Copy these sentences, choosing the correct words:

Colds are caused by **viruses/fungi** and food poisoning is caused by **bacteria/viruses**. Microbes can be **pathogen/transmitted** from one person to another.

KEY POINTS

- Microbes can be transmitted from one person to another.
- We can take action to avoid becoming infected.

C4 STOPPING THE SPREAD OF DISEASE

How can we stop diseases spreading?

If a disease spreads quickly and infects a lot of people, we call it an **epidemic**. The stories below describe how people tried to stop epidemics.

The Great Plague

About 400 years ago, a lot of people in London died from the plague. But people who lived in the countryside stayed healthy. One day in a Derbyshire village called Eyam, a parcel of cloth arrived from London. The tailor who opened the parcel died a few days later from the plague.

Many people wanted to leave the village because they were frightened. They thought that they would catch the plague. The vicar told them not to leave. He knew that they would spread the plague to other villages in the area. Over the next few months over 250 people in the village died from the plague. But because no one left the village, the plague did not spread to the rest of the countryside.

Look at the picture. It shows the gravestones of some of the people who died in the village.

a **How did the vicar stop the plague spreading to other villages?**

Cholera

In 1854 cholera broke out in London. People thought the disease was spread through the air. Dr John Snow disagreed. He thought it was spread by drinking polluted water.

He used four pieces of evidence to reach his conclusion.

1. People who caught cholera had all drunk water from the same well.
2. Workers in the local brewery who drank only beer did not catch the disease.

3. A woman who lived on the other side of London had a bottle of water sent to her from the well. She was the only person in her part of London to get the disease.
4. When Dr Snow stopped people from drinking water from the well, the disease quickly disappeared.

b What did Dr Snow do to stop the cholera from spreading?

Who helps to stop disease spreading?

If a dangerous disease broke out now, lots of different people would be involved in stopping it spreading.

c Look at the picture below. How many different types of people would help stop the disease from spreading?

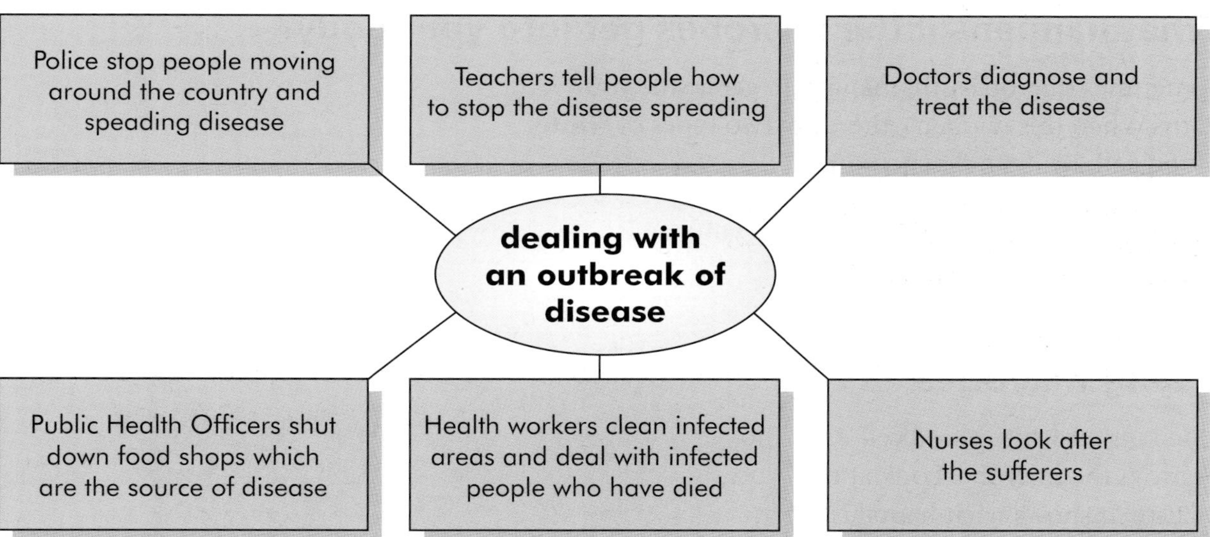

Police stop people moving around the country and speading disease
Teachers tell people how to stop the disease spreading
Doctors diagnose and treat the disease
dealing with an outbreak of disease
Public Health Officers shut down food shops which are the source of disease
Health workers clean infected areas and deal with infected people who have died
Nurses look after the sufferers

QUESTIONS

Copy these sentences and fill in the spaces using the words below:

drinking polluted stopping

The vicar of Eyam prevented the plague from spreading by ________ the villagers from leaving the village. Dr Snow prevented cholera from spreading by stopping the people ________ the ________ water from the well.

KEY POINTS

- Lots of different groups of people are involved in stopping the spread of a disease.

C5 PROTECTION AGAINST DISEASE: NATURAL DEFENCES

What stops microbes getting into your body?

There are lots of microbes that can cause disease. Your body needs to defend you against these microbes. Otherwise you would be ill most of the time. Your body defends you in many ways.

- Your skin stops microbes getting into the body.
- Your nose has hairs to catch microbes.
- Your windpipe is lined with sticky mucus. It traps microbes before they reach your lungs.
- Your eyes make tears that kill microbes and wash them away.

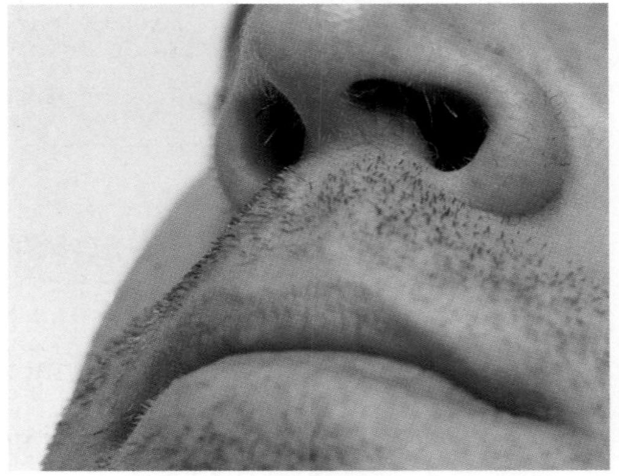

What happens if the microbes get into your body?

Sometimes microbes still manage to get inside your body. When this happens, there are two types of **white blood cell**, ready to defend you.

a What kind of blood cells defend your body against microbes?

Eating microbes

One kind of white blood cell 'eats' and destroys the microbe. Look at the picture. It shows what happens when bacteria enter through a wound and get into your blood.

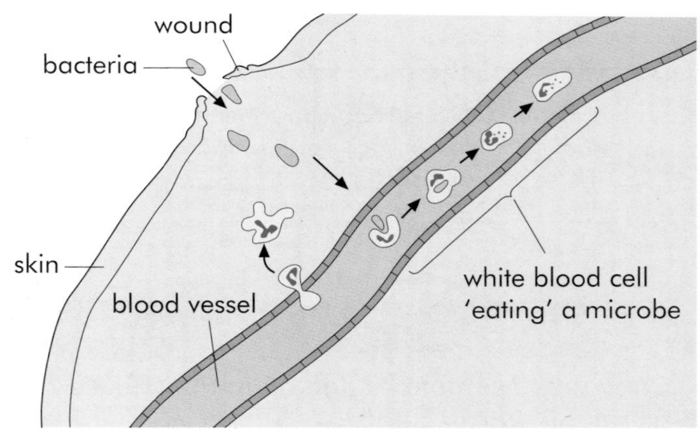

Making antibodies

Another kind of white blood cell makes chemicals called **antibodies**. The white blood cells make different antibodies to kill different kinds of microbes.

b What do some white blood cells make that kills microbes?

Antibodies destroy microbes in three different ways.

1. Some antibodies puncture the microbes and kill them.

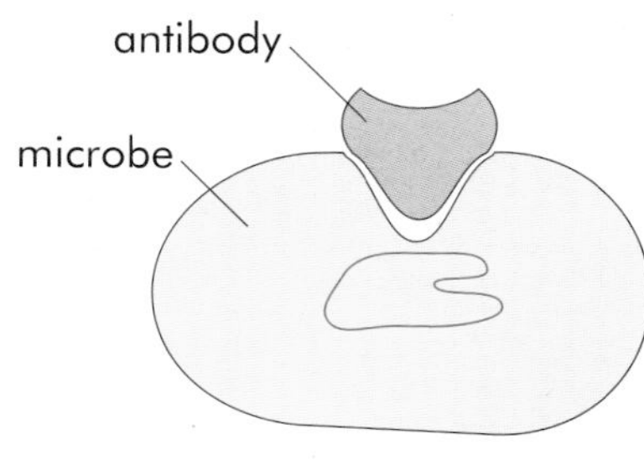

2. Some antibodies make the microbes stick together. This makes it easier for other white blood cells to find and eat them.

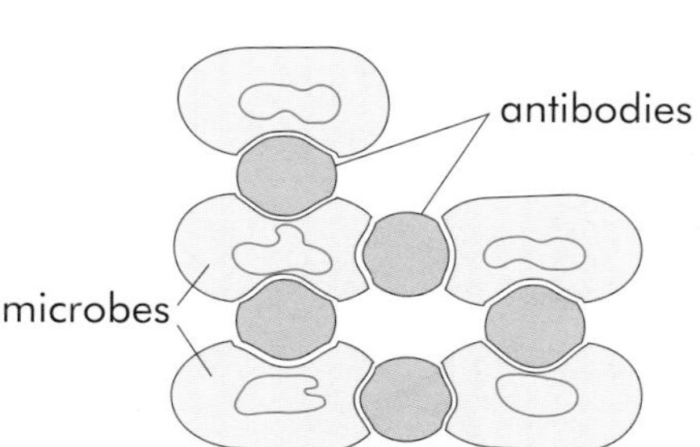

3. Some antibodies are like the police. They surround the microbe and make it harmless.

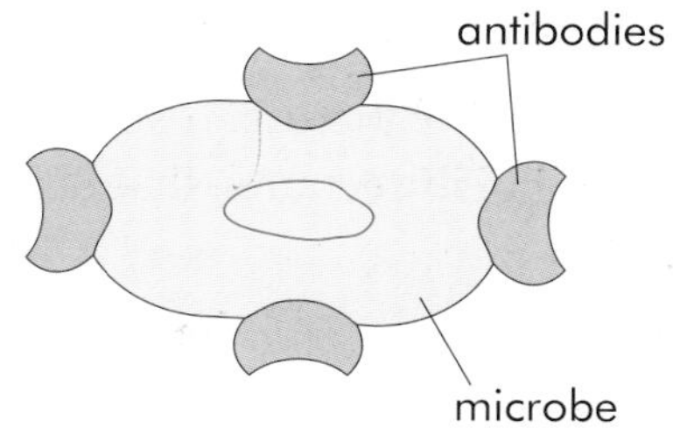

What else can make us ill?

We can become ill if we do not eat the right food. Look at the picture. The child has not eaten enough vitamin D. She has **rickets**. This makes the bones in her legs go soft and they bend.

We can also inherit diseases from our parents. **Cystic fibrosis** is a disease like this. It makes people produce thick mucus and they cannot breathe properly.

We cannot catch rickets or cystic fibrosis from other people because they are not caused by microbes.

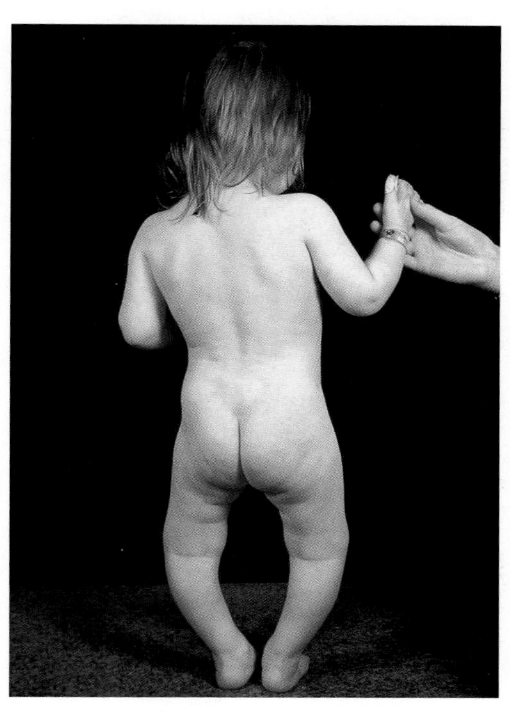

QUESTIONS

1 Write down three ways that your body stops microbes getting in.

2 Draw a diagram to show how white blood cells kill microbes.

KEY POINTS

- Your body has lots of defences against disease.
- Some diseases are not caused by microbes.

C6 PROTECTION AGAINST DISEASE: ANTIBIOTICS

How do scientists help us fight disease?

To stop us catching an infection, scientists have made lots of different chemicals. These chemicals are used to kill microbes while they are still outside our bodies.

Look at the picture. It shows some of the chemicals, called **disinfectants**, that kill microbes.

ⓐ What do we use disinfectants for?

We can test how good these chemicals are at killing microbes. We add a bit of the chemical to bacteria growing in a Petri dish.

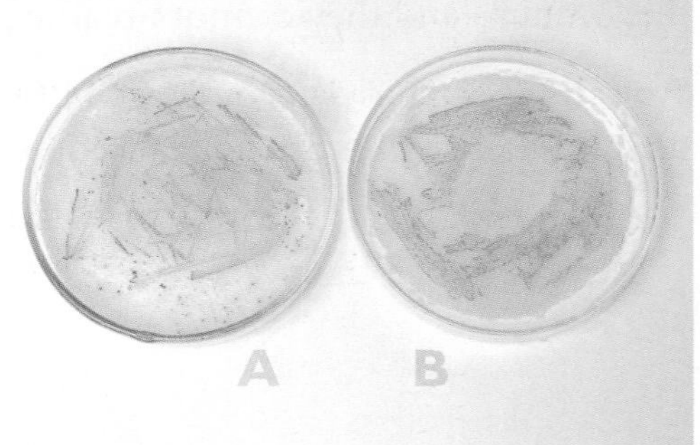

Look at the two Petri dishes. The same bacteria were growing on each of them. A drop of disinfectant was added to the middle of the plate on the right. The clear patch shows that the bacteria have died. The disinfectant has killed them.

What are antibiotics?

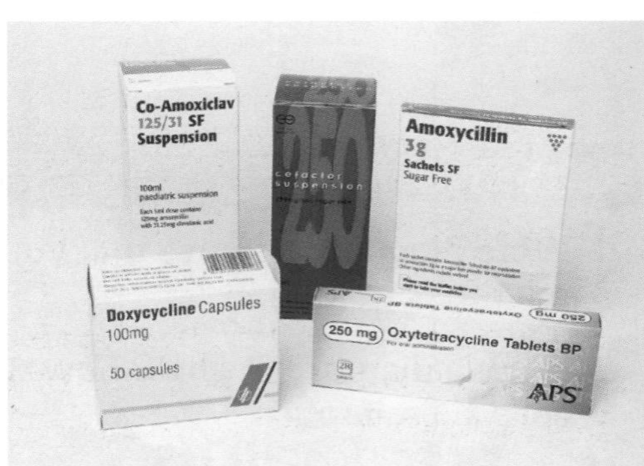

Antibiotics are medicines. They are not like disinfectants because they kill only bacteria, not other microbes. They work inside our bodies, not outside.

ⓑ How are antibiotics different from disinfectants?

We can only get antibiotics from a doctor. The doctor must fill in a form called a **prescription** before we can have the antibiotics. The photo shows a prescription.

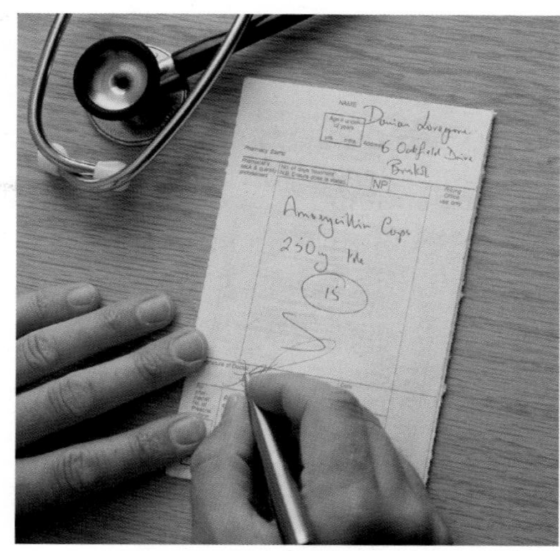

Antibiotics don't kill viruses

Antibiotics kill only bacteria. Colds are caused by viruses. This is why doctors do not give antibiotics to people who have a cold.

C **Why do doctors not give antibiotics to someone with a cold?**

What are the problems with antibiotics?

When antibiotics were first discovered, people thought diseases would be cured forever. But some bacteria have become **resistant** to antibiotics. This means that the antibiotic will no longer kill the bacteria.

In order to stop more bacteria becoming resistant to antibiotics, doctors:

- give antibiotics only to people who really need them
- make sure that even when people feel better, they finish taking the medicine. This makes sure that all the bacteria in their bodies are killed.

QUESTIONS

Copy these sentences, choosing the correct words:

Disinfectants kill microbes **inside/outside** your body. Antibiotics kill **bacteria/microbes** that are **inside/outside** your body.

KEY POINTS

- Disinfectants kill microbes outside our bodies.
- Antibiotics kill bacteria inside our bodies.

C7 THE HISTORY OF ANTIBIOTICS

Who discovered antibiotics?

The first antibiotic was called **penicillin**. Penicillin was discovered by Sir Alexander Fleming in 1928. He was growing some bacteria in a Petri dish. By accident, some fungus also grew on the plate. Fleming noticed that where the fungus was growing, the bacteria were dying. He realised that the fungus was producing a chemical that was killing the bacteria.

a What did Fleming realise when he saw the fungus killing the bacteria?

Look at the picture. Although it is hard to read, it shows a page from Fleming's note book. It describes what he saw in the Petri dish.

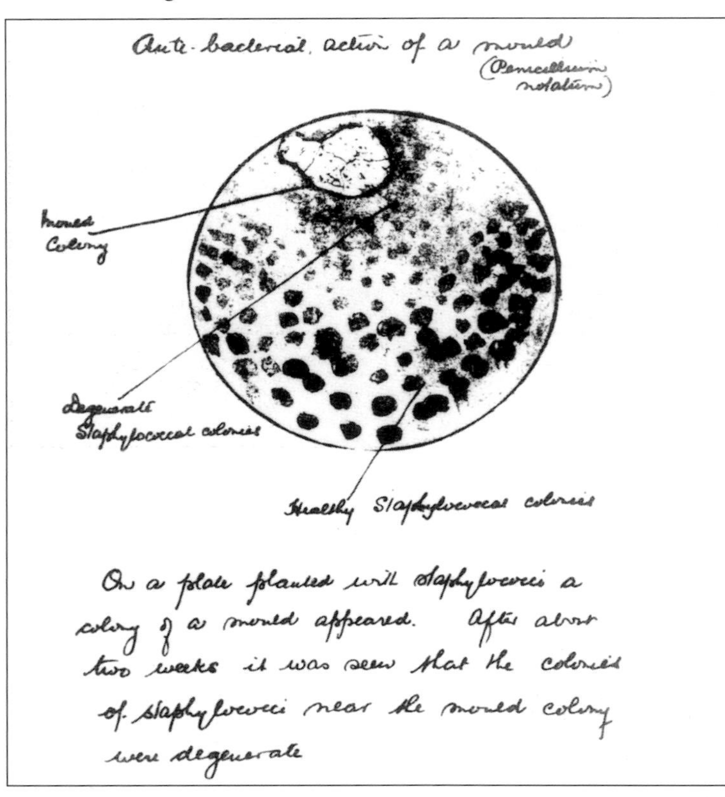

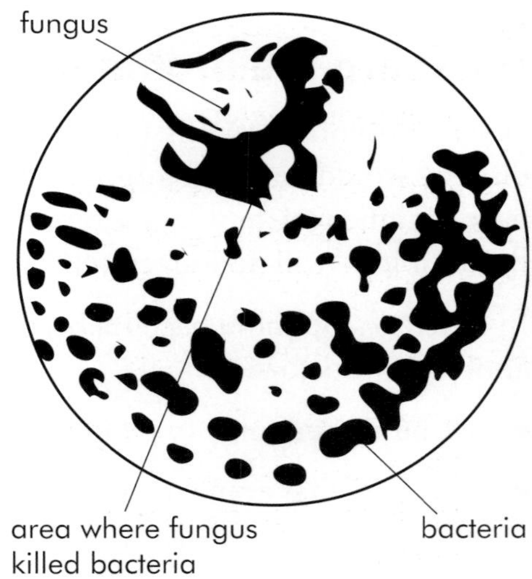

Some time later, in 1940, two scientists called Florey and Chain realised that the chemical from the fungus could treat people with diseases. They used the chemical called penicillin to treat soldiers with infected wounds during the Second World War. It saved many lives.

b What is the name of the antibiotic that Fleming discovered?

What effect have antibiotics had on disease?

Scientists have now made many more antibiotics. Some of them kill only one kind of bacteria. A good example is the antibiotic that kills the bacteria that cause the disease tuberculosis (TB).

TB spreads when people sneeze or cough. The disease gradually destroys the lungs and eventually causes death. There are two antibiotics that kill only the bacteria that cause TB. People with TB have to take the antibiotics for up to seven months before all the bacteria are killed.

Look at the graph. It shows how many people died from tuberculosis.

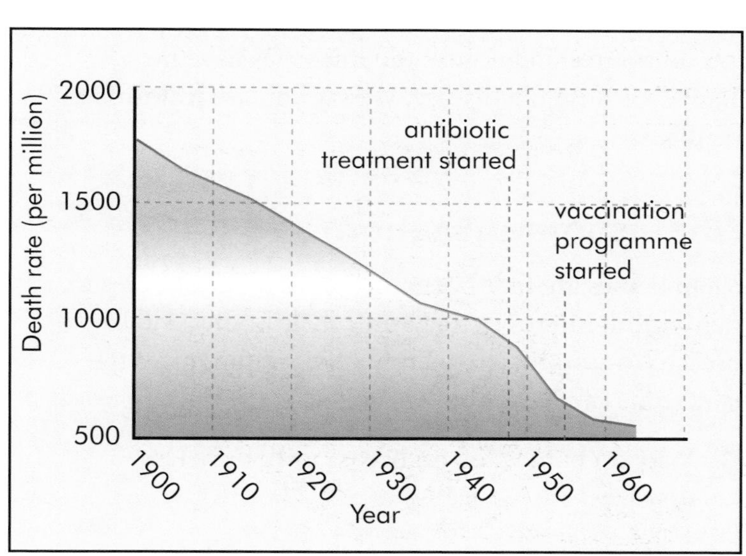

c What happened to the death rate from TB after antibiotic treatment started?

The graph shows that the death rate was already falling slowly before penicillin was first used. This was because housing and hospitals were getting better.

d Why was the death rate from TB already falling before antibiotic treatment was started?

QUESTIONS

Copy these sentences and fill in the spaces using the words below:

penicillin bacteria Fleming fungus

Sir Alexander ________ discovered the first antibiotic. He realised that a ________ on a Petri dish was killing the ________ growing there. Florey and Chain first used ________ as a medicine to treat people with diseases.

KEY POINTS

- Sir Alexander Fleming discovered the first antibiotic, called penicillin.

C8 PROTECTION AGAINST DISEASE: IMMUNITY AND IMMUNISATION

What is immunity?

When microbes enter your body, you make chemicals called **antibodies** to kill them. It takes several days to make the antibodies. During that time you suffer from the disease. When the antibodies kill the microbes, you get better.

But the antibodies stay in your blood after the illness. This means that when you catch the disease again, the antibodies are ready to kill the microbes straight away. You do not feel ill because the microbes have no chance to cause the disease. We say you are **immune** to the disease.

What is immunisation?

When babies are first born, they have no antibodies in their blood. Microbes that enter their bodies will cause disease. To stop this happening, the mother gives the baby some of her antibodies in her breast milk.

a Why do babies fed on breast milk have less diseases?

Immunisation is another way of stopping babies getting a disease. The baby is injected with a **vaccine**. The vaccine contains the microbes that cause the disease. But the microbes that are injected do not give the baby the disease because:

- the microbes may be dead
- the microbes may be weakened
- only bits of the microbe are injected.

So the baby makes antibodies without ever having the disease.

b Why doesn't a vaccine give the baby the disease?

When the baby comes into contact with the real microbe later on, the antibodies are there in the body ready to kill the microbe.

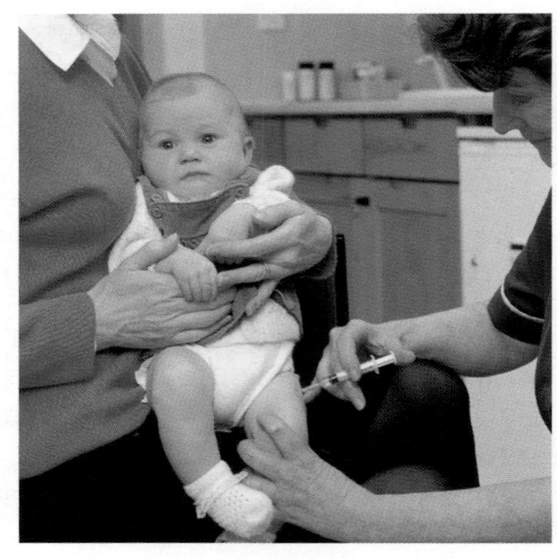

How have vaccines affected our health?

Vaccines can sometimes get rid of diseases completely. Look at the graph. It shows how many children died of a disease called diphtheria in different years from 1870 to 1960.

c In what year were all children immunised against diphtheria?

d How many children died of diphtheria in 1960?

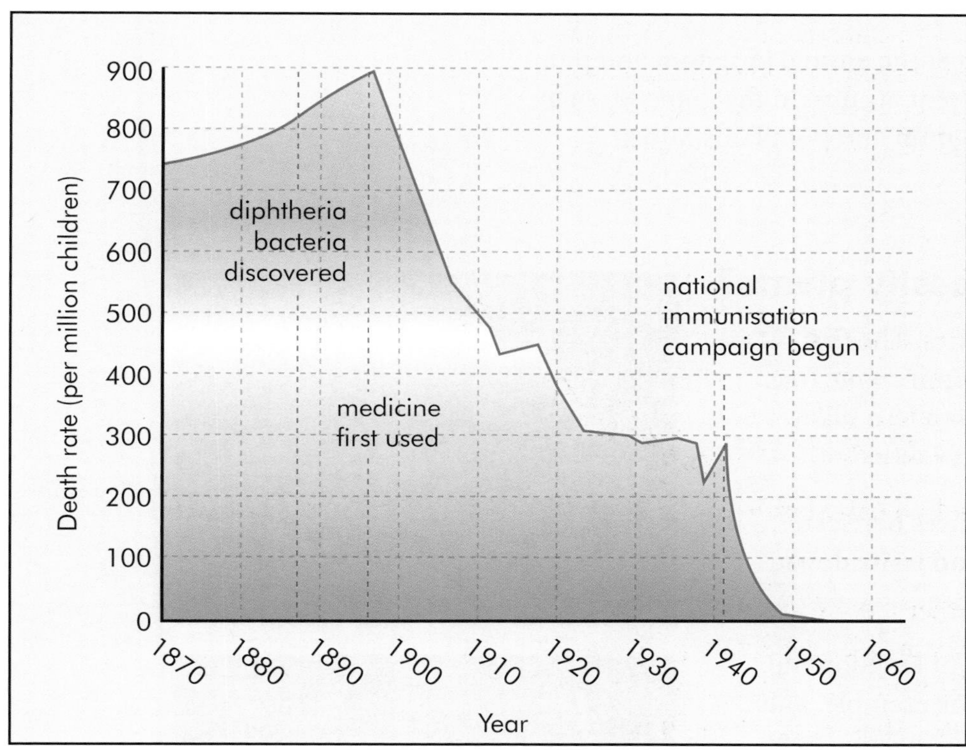

QUESTIONS

Find out which of the following diseases you have been immunised against.

- polio
- diphtheria
- whooping cough
- tetanus
- measles
- mumps
- rubella
- influenza
- TB

KEY POINTS

- Immunisation helps us to make antibodies against a disease.

D1 HOW ARE GREEN PLANTS CLASSIFIED?

How do we classify things?

All living things are different. It is these differences that help them to survive in different environments. But when we look carefully we find that groups of living organisms have some things in common.

In Unit 7D we looked at the **animal kingdom** and put the animals into different groups. In this topic we shall look at the **plant kingdom** and put plants into different groups.

How do we classify plants?

Look at the two pictures. The first one shows a branch from a pine tree. The second one shows a fern plant. The two plants are very different.

a **Look for differences between the two plants and write down as many as you can.**

We can divide the plant kingdom up in all sorts of ways. For example, one group could contain plants that have flowers and seeds to reproduce. The other group could contain plants that do not have flowers and seeds. We could divide each group up into even smaller groups. Scientists call this **classifying**.

How do scientists classify plants?

Scientists classify plants by looking at their features. The following plants have been put into groups based on the features they have in common.

Mosses and liverworts

- small
- tiny roots made of one cell
- no flowers
- reproduce without seeds
- live in damp shady places

Conifers

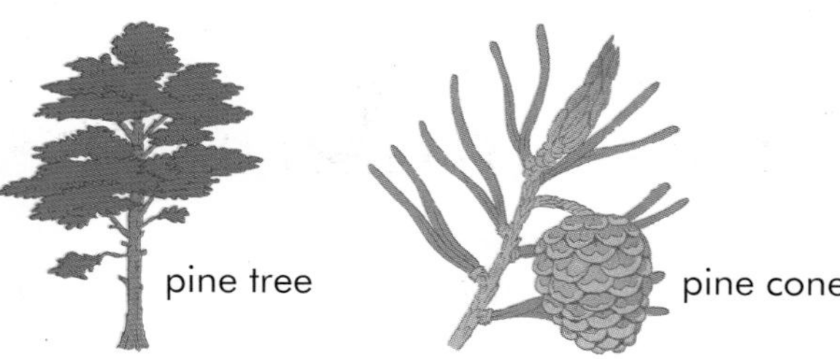

- very large
- no flowers
- reproduce with seeds
- seeds are inside cones
- live in all sorts of places

Ferns

- leaves coiled up when in bud
- no flowers
- reproduce without seeds
- live in damp places

Plants with flowers

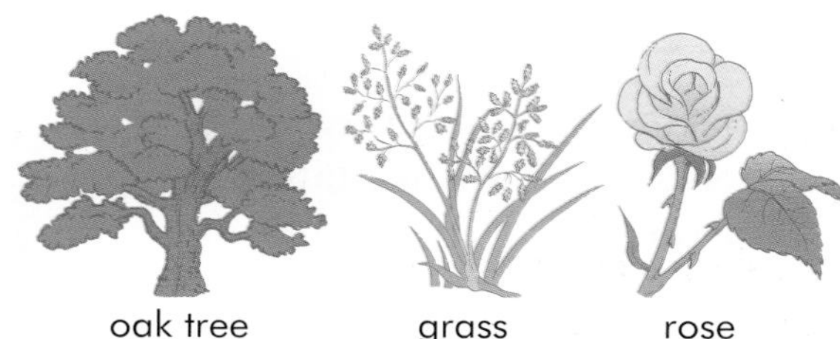

- flowers
- reproduce with seeds
- seeds are inside a fruit
- found almost everywhere

(b) Which group of plants have no flowers and have seeds inside cones?

(c) Which plant might you find in damp, shady places?

(d) Which plant has coiled up leaves when they first appear?

QUESTIONS

Copy these sentences and fill in the spaces using the words below:

cones damp flowers no

Ferns live in ________ places. Mosses have ________ flowers. Conifers have seeds inside ________ . Flowering plants have ________ .

KEY POINTS

- Scientists classify plants into groups by looking at their features.
- There are four main groups of plants: mosses and liverworts; conifers; ferns; and flowering plants.

D2 WHY ARE COMMUNITIES DIFFERENT IN DIFFERENT HABITATS?

What is a community?

You may have a community centre near your home. It is a building for all the different people who live in your area. The word **community** really means all the living things in a particular place.

Look at these two pictures. They show two different kinds of places. Scientists call different places **habitats**.

A habitat and all the things that live in it are called an **ecosystem**.

a **Make a list of the differences between the two habitats in the pictures.**

Different environmental conditions

All habitats are different. We can measure the differences between different habitats. The table shows some of the different **environmental conditions** that we could measure.

Water	Soil	Air
temperature	temperature	temperature
water speed	moisture	humidity
oxygen	acidity	light
light		wind speed

b **Look at this picture of the desert. Use the table to suggest what environmental conditions you would measure in this habitat.**

Environmental conditions will affect what lives in a habitat. For example, a frog needs lots of water. It could not live in a desert.

c Why could a fish not live in the air?

How do organisms adapt to environmental conditions?

Animals and plants have features that let them survive in a particular habitat.

- Caddis-fly larvae live in streams. They build a coat of small stones. This protects them and makes them hard to see.
- Water lilies have long stems. This lets the flowers float on the surface of the water. The stems are attached to the bed of the river. This stops them from being washed away.

A caddis-fly larva

d How is a water lily adapted to live in a river?

A water lily

QUESTIONS

1 Copy these sentences, choosing the correct words:

A community is all the organisms that **live/do not live** in a habitat. The organisms **are/are not** adapted to live in the habitat.

2 We can measure environmental conditions. Name three things we could measure.

KEY POINTS

- Different communities live in different habitats.
- Environmental conditions in a habitat affect what can live there.
- Organisms are adapted to live in a particular habitat.

D3 HOW BIG ARE THE POPULATIONS IN A HABITAT?

How can we find out a population size?

Imagine you wanted to find out how many daisies are on the school field. This is called the daisy **population**. You could go onto the field and count them all. But this would take you a very long time and be hard to do.

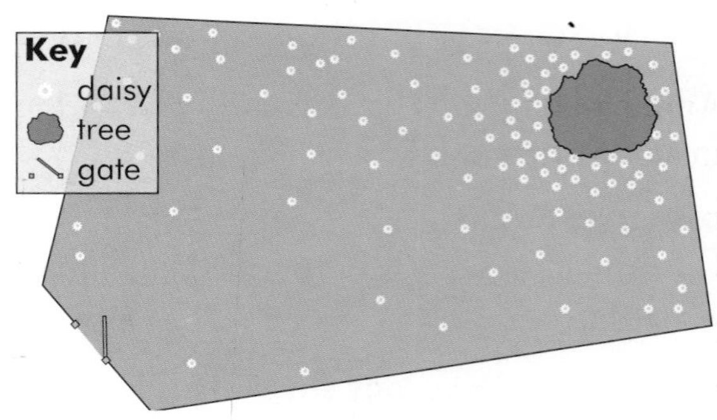

Counting beetles on the school field would be even harder. Unlike daisies, beetles do not stay in one place.

Because counting can be so difficult, we have to **sample** the field. This will give us an estimate of the size of the population.

Imagine the school field is 10 000 m^2. We could count the daisies in 1 m^2 and multiply our answer by 10 000. If we found 4 daisies in each 1 m^2, then we multiply 4 by 10 000. We would estimate that there would be 40 000 daisies on the school field.

What is a quadrat and how do we use it?

A **quadrat** is a frame that is 1 m^2. You throw it onto the field and count all the daisies inside the frame.

There can be a problem with using quadrats. Look at the picture at the top of the page. If Mary throws the quadrat near the tree, it will contain a lot of daisies.

a **What will happen if Mary throws the quadrat near the gate?**

Because there are more daisies near the tree and fewer daisies near the gate, Mary throws the quadrat several times in different places. Then she calculates the average number of daisies in the quadrats.

This is the data that Mary collected.

Quadrat number	Number of daisies
1	5
2	2
3	8
4	2
5	3

(b) What was the total number of daisies that Mary counted?

Mary calculates the average number of daisies in a quadrat by dividing the total number of daisies counted by the number of quadrats.

total number of daisies = 20
number of quadrats = 5

This means the average number of daisies in a quadrat is $20 \div 5 = 4$.

There are an average of 4 daisies in each quadrat.

(c) The school field is 10 000 m^2. Mary found an average of 4 daisies in each 1 m^2. Estimate how many daisies are in the school field.

QUESTIONS

Copy these sentences and fill in the spaces using the words below:

average   difficult   quadrat   sample

Counting all the daisies in a field can be very ________. To make it easier we ________ the field using a ________. We do this several times and work out the ________ number of daisies in each 1 m^2.

KEY POINTS

- Sampling is used to estimate the size of a population.

D4 HOW DO THINGS IN A COMMUNITY DEPEND ON EACH OTHER?

What affects population size?

Populations can only be large if the organisms have all the things they need. They need enough food and water, for example. But other things such as predators will reduce the size of the population.

The picture shows a lion eating a zebra. The population of zebra is kept down because lions eat some of them.

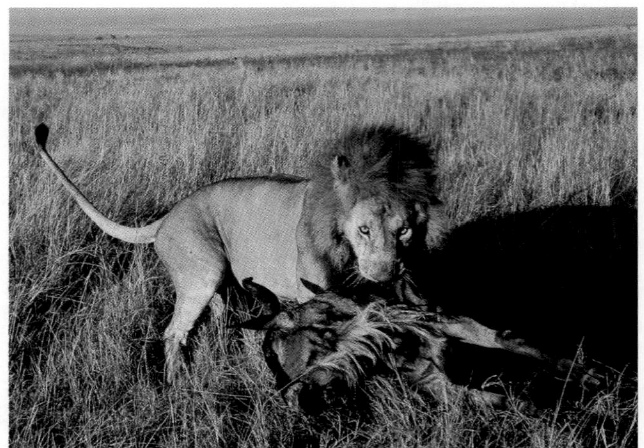

What does a food web show?

A **food web** is several **food chains** linked together. It shows what eats what in a habitat.

Food webs always begin with plants. Plants are **producers** because they produce food using sunlight. Animals are **consumers**. They consume food to get their energy.

Animals that eat plants are **primary consumers**. Animals that eat other animals are **secondary consumers**. Energy moves through the food chain from the Sun, to the producer, to the consumer.

a **Why are plants called producers?**

How do populations affect each other?

We can use food webs to work out how populations affect one another. Look at the food web. Think what would happen if someone cut down the oak tree.

- The leaf-eating insects would have no food and would die.
- The moths would have to eat more small plants to survive.

b **What would happen to the population of small plants if the oak tree were cut down?**

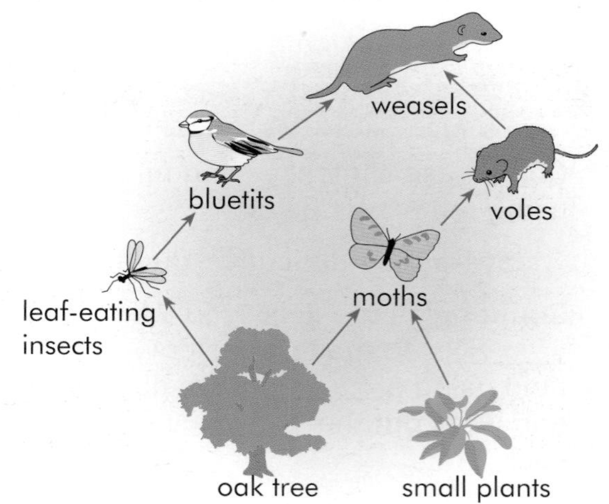

Changing the size of one population can change the size of other populations as well.

What causes changes in population size?

1. Changing the environment: a harsh winter can kill off many birds and plants.
2. Humans can affect population sizes. For example, if we use pesticides this will reduce the size of the pest population.
3. Pollution in rivers can poison fish.
4. Predators hunt food and reduce the size of a population.

When **predators** hunt for food, the size of the **prey** population drops. This means less food for the predator, so their population drops too.

With fewer predators, less prey will get eaten so their population rises. Look at the graph. It shows how the population of a predator (a lynx) and its prey (hares) go up and down every year.

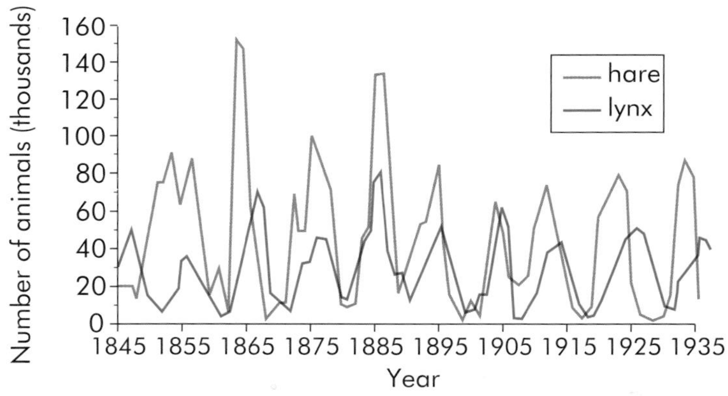

QUESTIONS

Copy these sentences and fill in the spaces using the words below:

size up webs

Changing the size of one population can affect the ________ of another population. We can use food ________ to show how one population affects another. Population sizes for predator and prey tend to go ________ and down.

KEY POINTS

- Changing the size of one population can cause changes in the size of other populations.
- We can use food webs to show how one population affects another.

D5 HOW CAN WE SHOW POPULATION NUMBERS?

What is a pyramid of numbers?

Look at the food chain.

grass	→	insects	→	bluetits
(100)		(20)		(1)

The numbers show the population size of each organism.

ⓐ What happens to the numbers as we go along the food chain?

You can see the numbers get smaller as we go along the food chain.

We can make the numbers easier to see if we draw a **pyramid of numbers.**

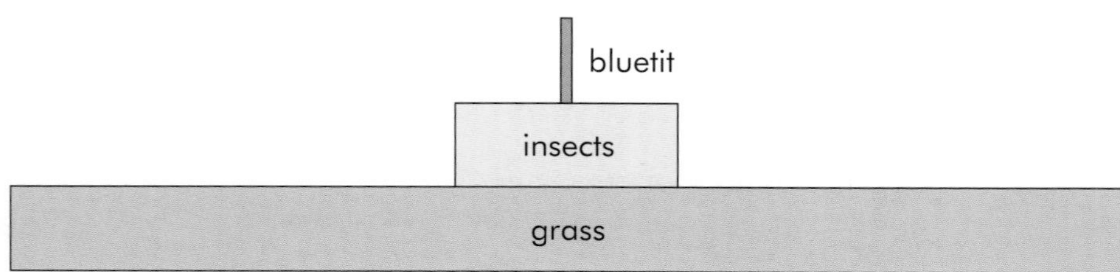

The higher the number, the bigger the box.

ⓑ Draw a pyramid of numbers for this food chain.

dead leaves	→	worms	→	blackbird
(200)		(4)		(1)

How does energy flow through a food chain?

There are more organisms at the bottom of the pyramid and fewer at the top.

This is because the organisms at the top of the pyramid feed on the ones lower down. At each step on the pyramid, some of the energy in the organisms is lost. Some energy is lost as heat and some is lost when animals get rid of waste material. This means less energy is available for the organisms higher up. So the pyramid gets smaller towards the top.

C How is energy lost from a food chain?

When is a pyramid not a pyramid?

Sometimes a pyramid of numbers looks rather silly. Look at this food chain and its pyramid of numbers.

oak tree (1) → caterpillar (60) → bluetit (2)

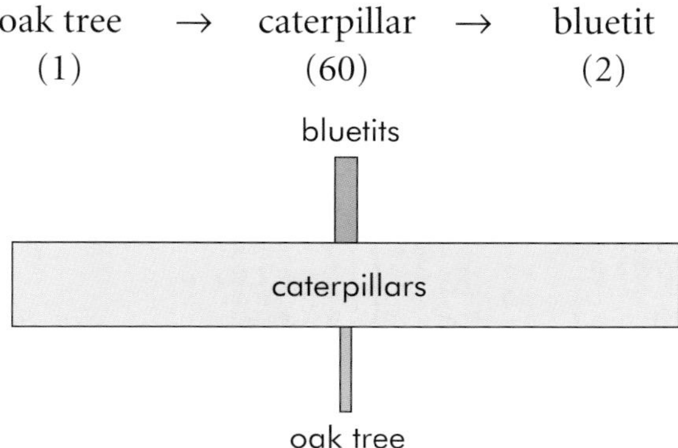

The pyramid has an odd shape because there is only one oak tree. But the oak tree is very big. Because it is so big it can make lots of food from sunlight and can feed lots of caterpillars. But the caterpillars feed only two bluetits.

QUESTIONS

Copy these sentences and fill in the spaces using the words below:

big pyramid smaller

We can show population sizes by using a ________ of numbers. Populations usually get ________ higher up the pyramid.

Sometimes the pyramid has an odd shape. This is because an organism is very ________ and can produce a lot of food for organisms higher up the pyramid.

KEY POINTS

- We can show population sizes using pyramids of numbers.
- Population sizes usually get smaller higher up the pyramid.
- There is less energy higher up in a pyramid of numbers.

E Atoms and elements

E1 HOW MANY DIFFERENT MATERIALS ARE THERE?

About materials

In science, the word 'material' has a special meaning. In everyday life it usually means a piece of cloth. In science it means anything that you can touch. Even a gas such as the air is a material.

Look at the pictures on this page. They are just a few of the different materials we know. For thousands of years people have looked for differences between materials. It was important for a cave man to know that wood would burn and bone would not.

No one knows how many different materials there are. We know there are at least several million. Scientists make new materials all the time. The number just keeps going up.

What are all the materials made from?

The English language has thousands of words. But they are all made up from just 26 letters. There are millions of materials, but they are all made up from about 100 building blocks. These building blocks are called **elements**.

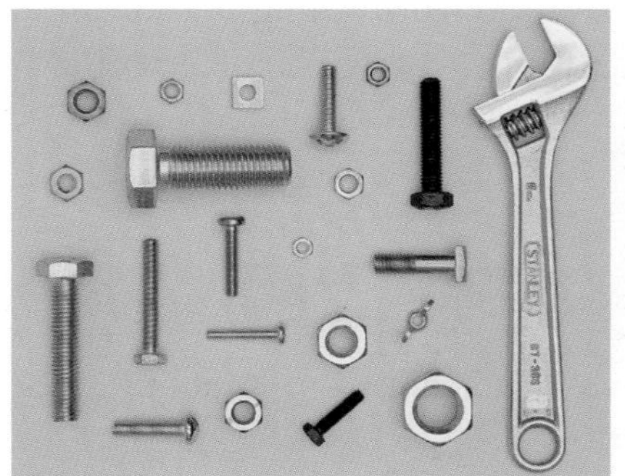

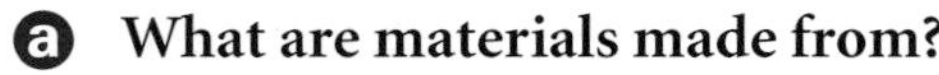

a What are materials made from?

We put letters together in different combinations to make different words. In the same way, elements are put together in different combinations to make different materials.

b Think of the word DOG. Can you rearrange the three letters in DOG to make a new word?

Look at the picture. It shows three different coloured building blocks. They have been put together in different ways.

C **Write down some more ways you could put the three coloured bricks together.**

In the same way, a group of elements can be put together in different ways to make different materials.

Some common elements

You may be surprised how many elements you already know. For example, hydrogen, oxygen, nitrogen, iron and gold are all different elements.

Look at the picture. It shows the names of most of the elements.

				H hydrogen													He helium
Li lithium	Be beryllium											B boron	C carbon	N nitrogen	O oxygen	F fluorine	Ne neon
Na sodium	Mg magnesium											Al aluminium	Si silicon	P phosphorus	S sulphur	Cl chlorine	Ar argon
K potassium	Ca calcium	Sc scandium	Ti titanium	V vanadium	Cr chromium	Mn manganese	Fe iron	Co cobalt	Ni nickel	Cu copper	Zn zinc	Ga gallium	Ge germanium	As arsenic	Se selenium	Br bromine	Kr krypton
Rb rubidium	Sr strontium	Y yttrium	Zr zirconium	Nb niobium	Mo molybdenum	Tc technetium	Ru ruthenium	Rh rhodium	Pd palladium	Ag silver	Cd cadmium	In indium	Sn tin	Sb antimony	Te tellurium	I iodine	Xe xenon
Cs caesium	Ba barium	La lanthanum	Hf hafnium	Ta tantalum	W tungsten	Re rhenium	Os osmium	Ir iridium	Pt platinum	Au gold	Hg mercury	Tl thallium	Pb lead	Bi bismuth	Po polonium	At astatine	Rn radon
Fr francium	Ra radium	Ac actinium															

QUESTIONS

Look for the names of the following elements in the picture above:

carbon hydrogen iron oxygen

Write down the letters that go with each name.

KEY POINTS

- All materials are made from combinations of different elements.

E2 WHAT ARE ELEMENTS MADE FROM?

What's in an element?

We saw on the last page that there are millions of different materials made from about 100 elements. But what makes an element an element?

Imagine you have a lump of the element called iron. To help understand why iron is an element, we are going to use a **model**.

Look at the picture. It is a model of what the lump of iron looks like. It is made up from bricks that are all the same.

If you take the model of a lump of iron apart, you end up with a pile of bricks that are all similar. In a real lump of iron, we call these bricks **atoms** of iron.

The model of a lump of iron is made from the same kind of bricks. The element iron is made up from atoms of iron that are all the same.

a **Which of the pictures A, B or C is not an element?**

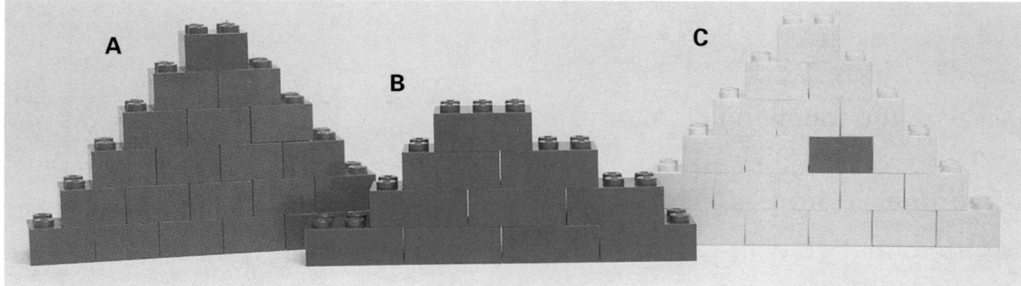

Elements and non-elements

Elements are made from just one kind of atom. Anything that is made from more than one kind of atom is called a non-element.

The element hydrogen is made from only hydrogen atoms. Instead of drawing a brick, we can draw the atom as a circle. The letter H stands for hydrogen, so we put the letter H inside the circle.

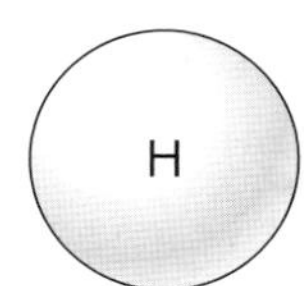

The element oxygen is made from only oxygen atoms. We can draw an oxygen atom in a similar way.

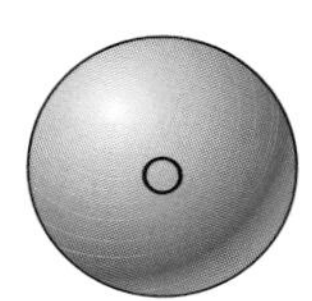

Water is a non-element. It is made from both hydrogen atoms and oxygen atoms joined together.

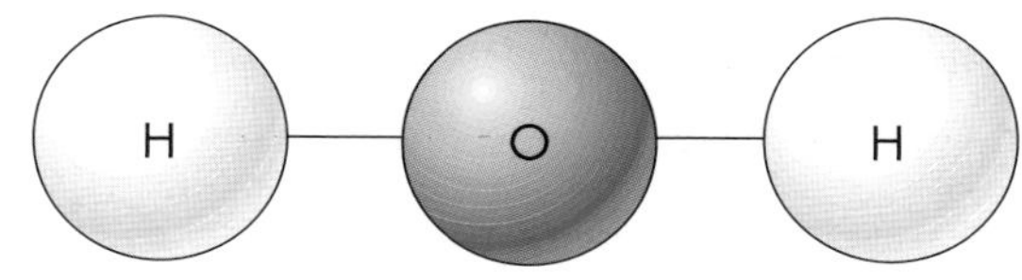

b **How many atoms of hydrogen are in water?**

c **How many atoms of oxygen are in water?**

How big are atoms?

Atoms are very small. They are much too small to see with the microscopes we use at school.

Scientists use models to understand how atoms are put together to make materials. It is a bit like Lego, but these models are made from balls instead of brick shapes. Look at the picture. It is a model of a sugar called glucose.

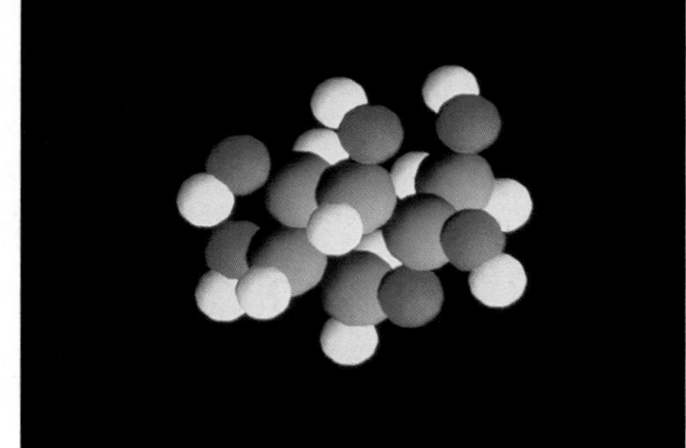

d **Is glucose an element or a non-element?**

QUESTIONS

Copy these sentences, choosing the correct words:

Elements are made from atoms that are **different kinds/all one kind**. Materials made from different kinds of atoms are called **elements/non-elements**.

KEY POINTS

- Elements are made up from one kind of atom.

WHAT ARE ELEMENTS LIKE?

Who found out about elements?

The first elements to be discovered were materials like gold, silver, carbon and sulphur. People did not realise that they were elements. It was not until about 200 years ago that scientists realised that they were elements.

Before that time scientists were very secretive. To prevent other people finding out about their discoveries about elements, they wrote them down in code. Look at the picture. It shows the code used by some of the scientists.

ELEMENTS

Element	W.t	Element	W.t
Hydrogen	1	Strontian	46
Azote	5	Barytes	68
Carbon	5.4	Iron	50
Oxygen	7	Zinc	56
Phosphorus	9	Copper	56
Sulphur	13	Lead	90
Magnesia	20	Silver	190
Lime	24	Gold	190
Soda	28	Platina	190
Potash	42	Mercury	167

a **Why did some scientists write their discoveries down in code?**

We now know much more about the elements and how they behave. Scientists now share this useful information.

How are elements different?

When scientists looked at the elements, they found that some were very different from others. They also found that some were very similar. The ways elements look and behave are called their **properties**. The scientists tried to classify the elements according to their properties.

A

Some of the properties scientists use to classify elements include:

- appearance
- whether it is a solid, liquid or gas
- what temperature it melts or boils at
- whether it is a metal or a non-metal
- whether it is magnetic or non-magnetic.

b **Look at the pictures. Are these three elements solids, liquids or gases?**

B

C

How are the elements organised in the Periodic Table?

You have seen this table of elements before. It is called the **Periodic Table**. The elements are arranged into groups with similar properties. If we colour all the boxes that contain metals orange, and the non-metals yellow, the Periodic Table looks like this.

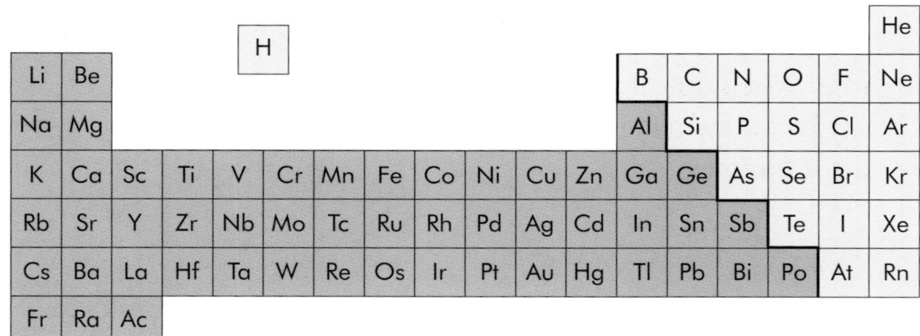

c **Whereabouts in the Periodic Table are all the non-metals, top, bottom, left or right?**

If we colour solids, liquid and gases different colours, the Periodic Table looks like this.

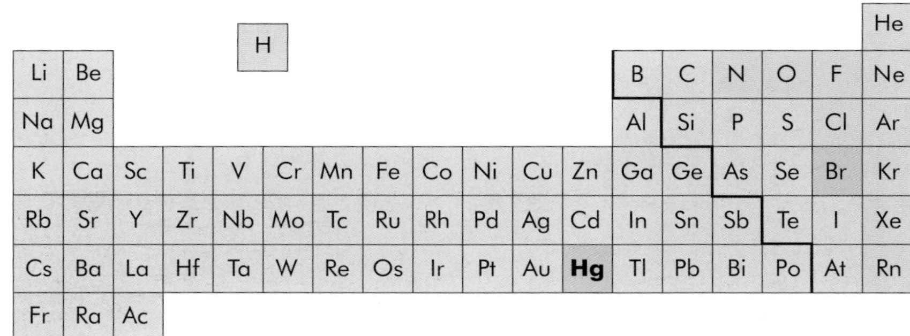

d **Hg stands for mercury. It is a liquid. Is mercury a metal or a non-metal?**

QUESTIONS

Copy these sentences and fill in the spaces using the words below:

groups Periodic properties

Elements that look similar have similar ________ . Scientists put elements with similar properties into ________ . Metals are found on the left-hand side of the ________ Table.

KEY POINTS

- Elements with similar properties are put into groups.
- Metals are found on the left of the Periodic Table and non-metals on the right.

E4 HOW DO WE GET ALL THE OTHER MATERIALS?

How are non-elements formed?

When different kinds of atom join together, they form non-elements. The new material is often very different from the elements that it is made from.

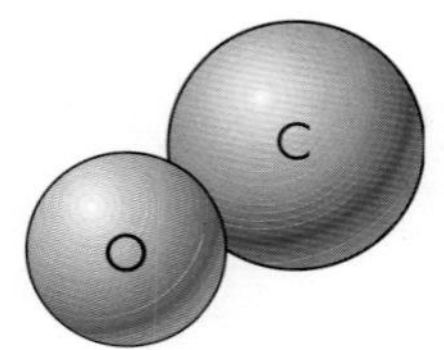

For example, carbon is a black solid. Oxygen is a colourless gas that we need to breathe. When one atom of carbon joins with one atom of oxygen, they make carbon monoxide. This is a very poisonous gas.

Carbon

+

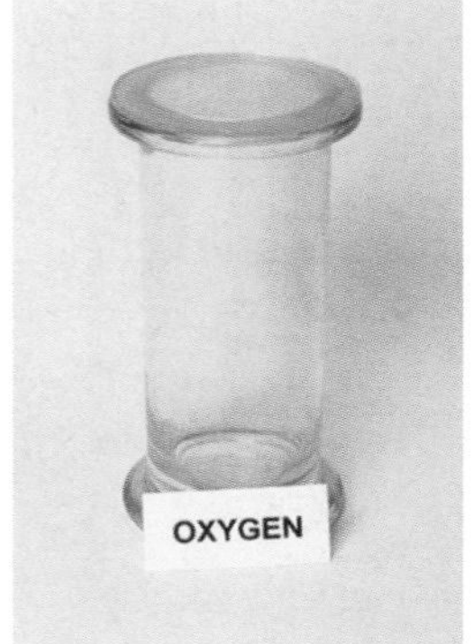

→

a How is carbon monoxide different from carbon and oxygen?

Water is made when two atoms of hydrogen join with one atom of oxygen. Both hydrogen and oxygen are gases. But water is a liquid.

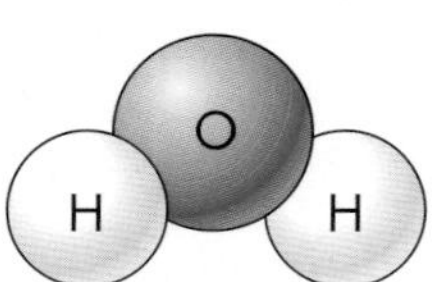

b How is water different from hydrogen and oxygen?

Scientists have a special name for non-elements like carbon monoxide and water. Non-elements made of more than one kind of atom are called **compounds**.

c What is the special name scientists have for non-elements?

What is a compound?

A compound is made up of groups of different atoms that are joined together. These groups of atoms are called **molecules**.

Water is a compound because it is made of hydrogen atoms joined to oxygen atoms.

When can an element be a molecule?

Some elements have atoms that join up into pairs. Oxygen is a good example. A pair of oxygen atoms join to form a molecule of oxygen. The pictures show this.

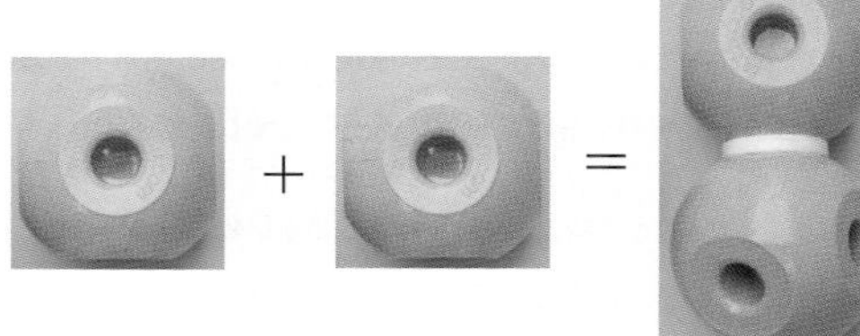

d What is a molecule of oxygen made of?

This is an atom. It is carbon.
Carbon is an element.

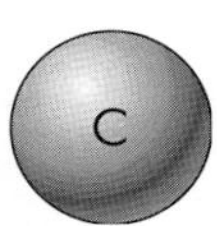

This is a molecule.
It is carbon dioxide.

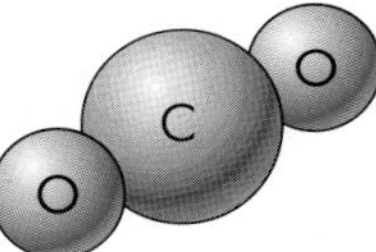

This is a molecule of oxygen.
It is an element.

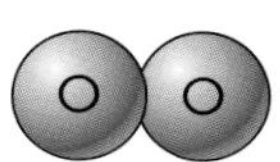

This is the compound carbon dioxide.

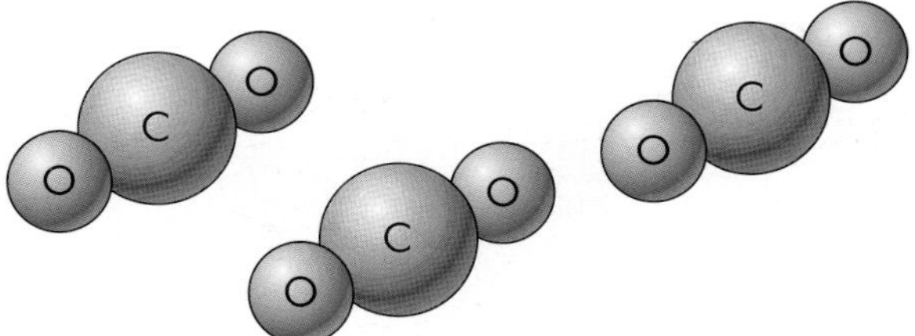

e How many molecules of the compound are shown opposite?

QUESTIONS

Copy these sentences and fill in the spaces using the words below:

atom compounds molecule

________ such as water are formed when different kinds of ________ join together. The smallest bit of a compound such as water is called a ________ .

KEY POINTS

- Compounds are formed when different kinds of atom join together.
- The smallest bit of a compound such as water is a molecule.

E5 HOW CAN WE RECORD THE CHANGES WHEN ATOMS JOIN?

What happens when atoms join?

When two different kinds of atom join together, a **chemical reaction** takes place. The material we end up with is always different from the two types of material we started with.

a What do we call the process when two different kinds of atom join together?

Look at the picture of the sparkler. It is a chemical reaction. Atoms of iron are joining with atoms of oxygen.

We started with a grey sparkler. We end up with a black burnt stick. We started with iron and oxygen. We end up with iron oxide.

In this picture, pink copper is reacting with yellow sulphur to make black copper sulphide.

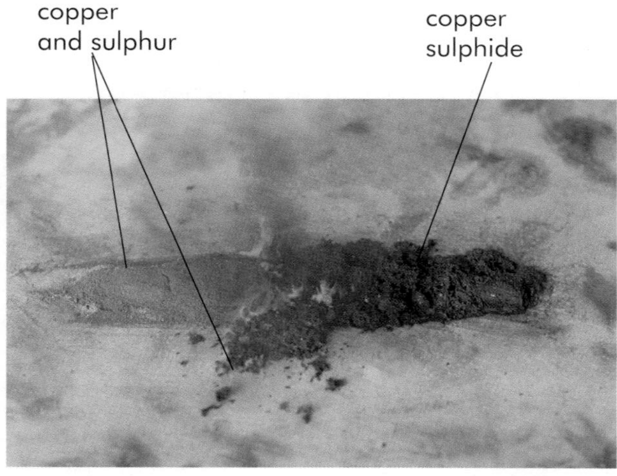

How can we record these changes?

We could just write a description of what we see. This might be quite long. There is a shorter way. Scientists use **equations**. Equations are useful because people all around the world can understand them.

b Why do scientists use equations?

Word equations

Think about the reaction between carbon and oxygen. We could write down:

Carbon reacts with oxygen to make carbon monoxide.

A simpler way of writing it would be to get rid of some of the words. We could replace 'reacts with' by a '+' sign. We could replace 'to make' with an arrow: '→'.

Our record of the reaction now looks like this:

carbon + oxygen → carbon monoxide

This is a **word equation**.

c **Write down the word equation for: Hydrogen reacts with oxygen to form water.**

Models

Scientists sometimes use **models** to show what happens during a chemical reaction. Look at the pictures. This is another way of showing what happens when carbon reacts with oxygen. In the model the carbon atom is black. The oxygen atom is white.

+

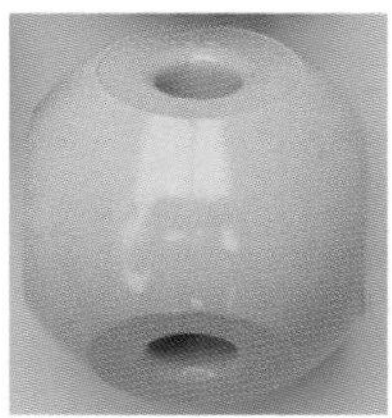

→

d **Do you prefer using word equations or models?**

QUESTIONS

Copy these sentences and fill in the spaces using the words below:

chemical   different   equations

When two ________ kinds of atom join together, a ________ reaction takes place. Scientists record these reactions using ________ .

KEY POINTS

- Scientists use equations to record what happens in a chemical reaction.

GETTING AHEAD OF THE GAME

Can we predict how elements will react?

We know that some elements have similar properties to other elements. We can use this knowledge to help us predict what will happen in a chemical reaction.

In the last topic we looked at how iron reacts with oxygen to form iron oxide in a sparkler.

iron + oxygen → iron oxide

Fe + O → Fe O

This information can help us predict what will happen if we use a similar element.

Like iron, copper is also a metal. When oxygen reacts with a metal, an oxide is formed.

a Copy and complete the word equation for copper reacting with oxygen:

copper + oxygen → ________

What's in a compound?

We can predict what will be formed when two different kinds of atom join together. In the same way, we can sometimes predict what kinds of atom are present in a compound.

The chemical name for salt is **sodium chloride.** We could predict that salt contains an element called **sodium.** It also contains the element chlorine. This joins with the sodium to make sodium chloride.

Sometimes it is not so easy. Water is made from hydrogen and oxygen. But there is no clue in the name to suggest that water contains either of them.

b Predict an element that is found in carbon monoxide.

What's in what?

Scientists soon realised what an enormous number of materials there are. They needed to name them so that other scientists would know what they were made from. Not everybody uses these names. People sometimes put **salt** on their food. But scientists would call it **sodium chloride**. This name tells other scientists what elements are in it.

Look at the picture. To a scientist it is a mixture of hydrogen oxide, carbon dioxide and citric acid. Most people just call it lemonade.

c Why do scientists use six different words to describe lemonade?

The table shows some clues for working out which elements are in different materials.

d Iron sulphide contains two elements. What are they?

Material or chemical name	Element
chloride	chlorine
oxide	oxygen
sulphide	sulphur

QUESTIONS

Copy these sentences and fill in the spaces using the words below:

elements   predict

We can ________ how similar elements will react. We can also predict which ________ are in different materials, using their names.

KEY POINTS

- We can predict how elements with similar properties will react.
- We can predict, from their names, what elements some materials contain.

F Compounds and mixtures

F1 ALL ABOUT ELEMENTS AND COMPOUNDS

What kinds of atom are in elements and compounds?

In Unit 8E you learned that all the atoms in an element are exactly the same. You also learned that materials that contain different kinds of atom are called compounds.

Look at the picture. It shows nitrogen oxide. Nitrogen oxide is a compound.

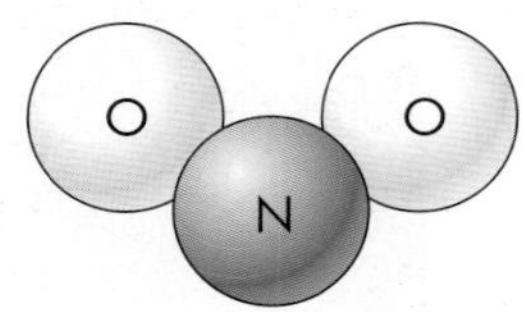

a How many different kinds of atom does it contain?

How many atoms are there in a compound?

Different compounds contain different numbers of atoms. There are millions of different compounds. They have different numbers of atoms in them.

Just as different letters make different words, different atoms make different compounds. Even when we make words from the same letters, they can mean different things.

TOT TOOT

These words both contain 'T' and 'O' but they mean very different things.

In the same way, different compounds can be made from the same atoms.

Look at the two compounds. They contain the same kinds of atom, but they are very different. The first one is water. You could drink it. But the second one is poisonous.

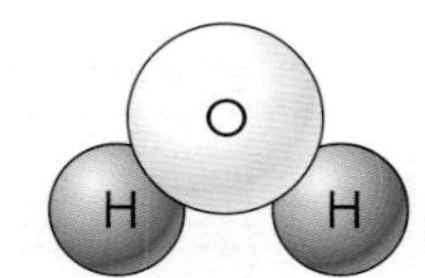

Water (hydrogen oxide)

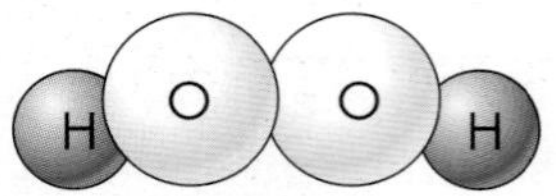

Hydrogen peroxide

b What two kinds of atom do the two compounds contain?

Writing a chemical formula

In Unit 8E, you saw that scientists sometimes use a letter rather than writing out the whole name of the element. When we use letters to stand for an element, they are called **symbols**.

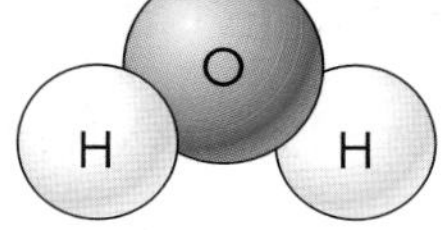

Look at the model for water. It contains two **H**s and one **O**. **H** stands for Hydrogen. **O** stands for Oxygen.

Instead of writing hydrogen oxide, we could write **HHO**. To make it even simpler, we write the number of each atom after the symbol. Because there are two **H**s and only one **O**, scientists would write $\mathbf{H_2O}$. If there is only one atom, we do not bother to write the number 1 after the symbol.

We call H_2O a **chemical formula**. The chemical formula for a particular compound is always the same.

We can show water as: 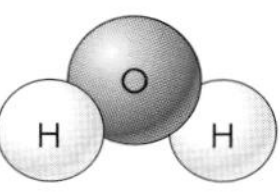 or $\mathbf{H_2O}$

C **Look at the formula for nitrogen oxide:**

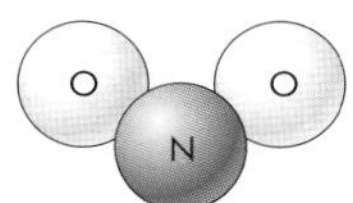 or $\mathbf{NO_2}$

How many atoms of O (oxygen) are there?

QUESTIONS

1 Copy these sentences and fill in the spaces using the words below:

atoms symbol

We can use a ________ to represent each element. The chemical formula tells us how many ________ are in each compound.

2 Look at the formula below. Write down the ones that are compounds.

H_2 O_2 CO_2 S_8 NO_2

KEY POINTS

- Scientists use symbols for the elements.
- The chemical formula shows how many atoms are in a compound.

F2 HOW DO COMPOUNDS DIFFER FROM THE ELEMENTS IN THEM?

Are the properties of elements and compounds the same?

In Unit 8E you saw that elements are often very different from the compounds they form.

Look at the picture. It shows two compounds. They both contain the same kinds of atom. The top one is water. The bottom one is called hydrogen peroxide. They are both liquids. But if you pour water on your hair it just gets wet. If you pour hydrogen peroxide on your hair it **bleaches** it blonde.

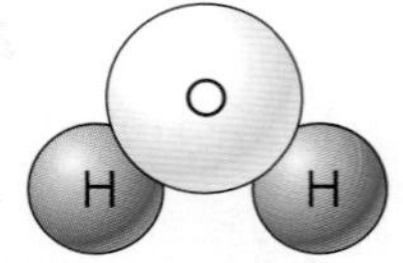

Water (hydrogen oxide)

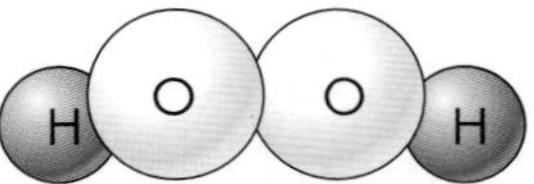

Hydrogen peroxide

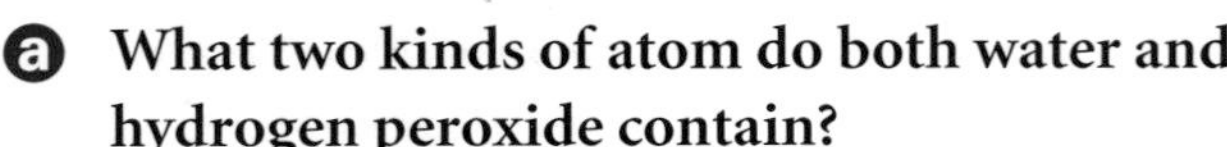

a What two kinds of atom do both water and hydrogen peroxide contain?

Hydrogen peroxide may be made out of the same elements as water but it bleaches hair blonde. The two compounds have similar properties – they are both liquids. They have some different properties – only hydrogen peroxide bleaches.

Hydrogen peroxide bleaches hair.

Why are elements and compounds different?

In a compound, elements don't just mix together. They join together. This means they make a very different new substance.

It's a bit like making a cake. You mix butter, flour, sugar and eggs together and get a sticky mess. But when you bake it, it turns into a delicious cake.

Mix butter, flour, eggs and sugar → sticky mess

→ bake it in the oven

→ delicious cake

Water

Water is made from oxygen and hydrogen. Oxygen is a colourless gas that we need to breathe. Hydrogen is a colourless gas that explodes when lit. When we join them together, we get water.

A gas jar of oxygen

Hydrogen is explosive!

Water is a harmless liquid.

oxygen + hydrogen → water

ⓑ What do we get when we join oxygen and hydrogen atoms together?

Sulphur dioxide

Sulphur is a bright yellow solid. The photo shows sulphur.

Sulphur dioxide is a choking gas. You may have smelt it if you have emptied ashes from a fire. Look at the picture opposite. Sulphur dioxide is made when sulphur and oxygen join together.

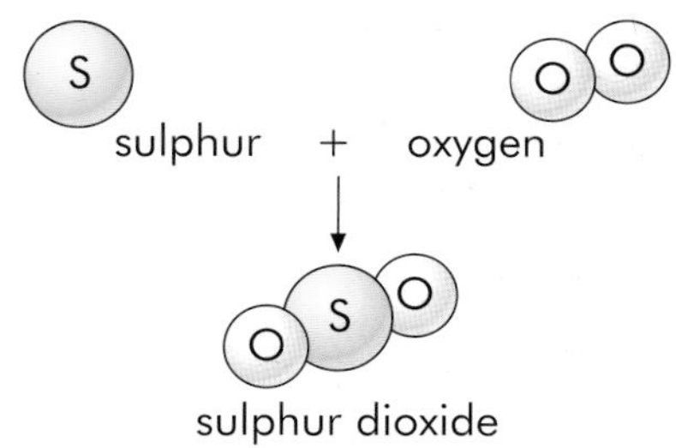

QUESTIONS

Copy these sentences, choosing the correct words:

Compounds are made from **different/the same** elements. The properties of compounds are **the same as/different from** the elements that make them.

KEY POINTS

- Compounds have different properties from the elements that make them.

F3 DO COMPOUNDS REACT CHEMICALLY?

What is a chemical change?

A **chemical change** happens when two different substances react together. Hydrogen reacting with oxygen to form water is a chemical change.

How can we tell if a chemical change has happened?

Chemical changes always involve at least two different materials. If the change involves only one material, it is not a chemical change. So water changing to ice or steam is not a chemical change. Water, ice and steam are all made up of water molecules.

a Is chocolate changing to melted chocolate a chemical change?

Look at the questions in the box below. If the answer to any of them is 'yes' then a chemical change has probably taken place.

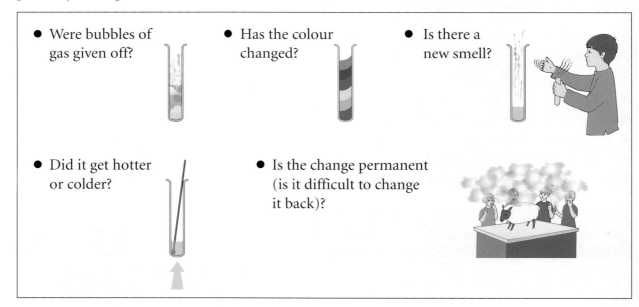

- Were bubbles of gas given off?
- Has the colour changed?
- Is there a new smell?
- Did it get hotter or colder?
- Is the change permanent (is it difficult to change it back)?

b Think about burning a match in air. Look at the box above. Is burning a match a chemical change?

Can compounds change?

Gill carried out an experiment with two compounds. She added magnesium carbonate to hydrochloric acid. The photos show what she saw.

This is what she wrote down in her notebook.

REACTANTS: Hydrochloric acid - colourless liquid
magnesium carbonate - white powder

OBSERVATIONS: Fizzing seen as soon as chemicals mixed - gas given off.
Bubbles were 4 cm deep (maximum)
Fizzing stopped after 23 sec.
Clear solution left in tube.

WHY WAS THIS A CHEMICAL CHANGE?
A gas was given off - new substance made.
Change appears permanent.

C **Why did she think a chemical change had happened?**

How do we report what we saw?

The things we see when we watch a chemical reaction are called **observations**. It is important to write them down carefully. Write down:

- which chemicals were reacting
- what they looked like before the reaction
- what you saw happening
- how the substances looked after the reaction
- why you think a chemical reaction has taken place.

QUESTIONS

Copy these sentences and fill in the spaces using the words below:

difficult substance two

A chemical change involves ________ or more materials. Chemical changes are always ________ to change back. A new ________ is always made.

KEY POINTS

- A new substance is always made during a chemical reaction.
- There are several ways of telling when a chemical change has happened.

F4 COMPOUNDS AND MIXTURES

Are compounds and mixtures the same?

You now know the differences between elements and compounds. But what are the differences between **mixtures** and compounds?

Even though a compound contains at least two different kinds of atom, it is not a mixture. You can use the information below to decide whether something is a mixture or not.

Mixtures

- Substances in a mixture are not joined together.
- Substances in a mixture are easy to separate.
- Mixtures contain at least two different substances mixed up together.

Compounds

- Atoms in a compound are joined together.
- It is very difficult to separate the atoms in a compound.
- Compounds have at least two different kinds of atom joined together.

a **Are mixtures and compounds the same? Answer yes or no.**

Look at the picture. It shows a mixture of two different kinds of compound. Even though there are four molecules in the picture, there are only two different kinds of compound.

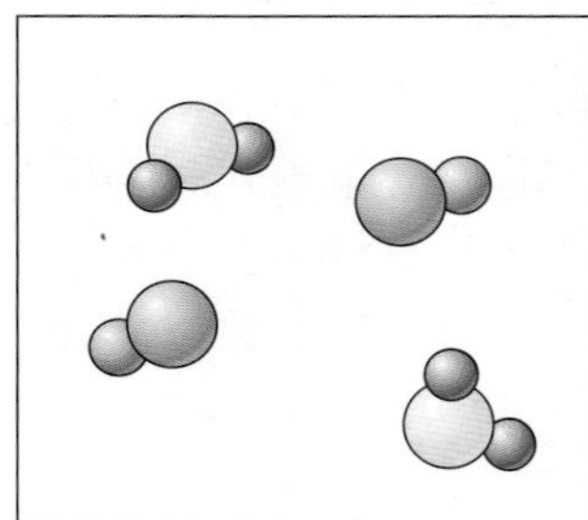

b **Look at the picture. It shows a mixture. How many different kinds of molecule are in the picture?**

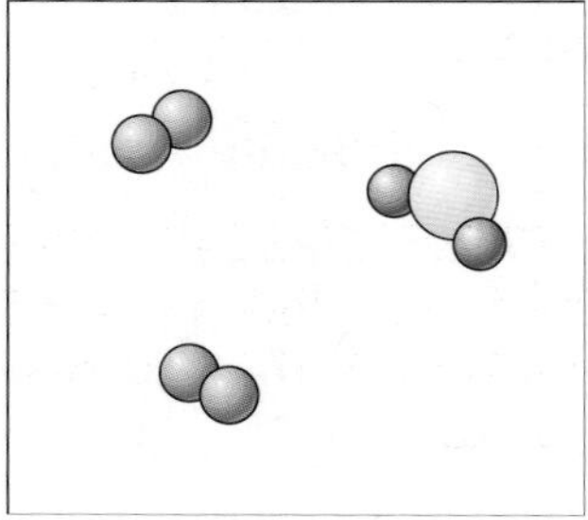

Is air a mixture?

Look at the picture. It shows all the different substances found in air.

Air is a mixture of different kinds of gases. The main substances are nitrogen (78%) and oxygen (21%).

C Is air a mixture?

You can see that the different substances in air are not joined together. Air is a mixture of different substances that can easily be separated. If you look carefully at the picture you will see one of the substances in air is:

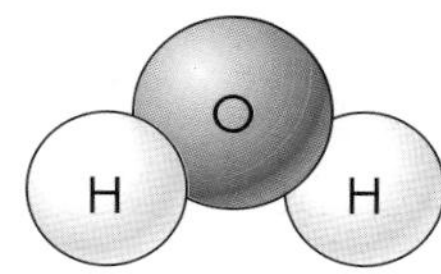

You may remember that this substance is water. We often see this substance separating easily from the rest of the mixture. If you see condensation on a cold window, this is water separating out from the rest of the air.

How do we use substances in the air?

Air contains many useful substances.

- Oxygen is used in hospitals to help patients breathe.
- Nitrogen is used for making fertilisers for farmers.
- Helium is useful because it is lighter than air so it is good for balloons.

QUESTIONS

Copy these sentences and fill in the spaces using the words below:

joined mixture separate

In a mixture the substances are not _______ together. In a compound the atoms are joined together and it is difficult to _______ them. Air is a _______ .

KEY POINTS

- Mixtures and compounds are different.
- Air is a mixture. It contains many useful substances.

F5 MORE DIFFERENCES BETWEEN COMPOUNDS AND MIXTURES

Melting and boiling points

What is a melting point?

Think about water. When water gets very cold, it turns to ice. We call this **freezing**. When it warms up it turns back to water. We call this **melting**.

The temperature that water melts at is the same as the temperature it freezes at. Scientists call this temperature its **melting point**. They could also have called this temperature its freezing point, but they just use the one description – **melting point**.

What is a boiling point?

When water boils, it turns to steam. When it cools down it condenses back to water. The temperature that water boils at is the same as the temperature it condenses at. Scientists call this temperature the **boiling point** of water.

a **Can you think of another name we could have used instead of boiling point?**

Pure substances have fixed melting and boiling points

In science, **pure** means not mixed with anything else. Pure water has nothing else in it except water.

Every pure substance has a fixed melting point and a fixed boiling point. This means that the melting and boiling points for a pure substance do not change. Pure water always melts at 0 °C and boils at 100 °C.

b **What are the melting point and the boiling point of pure water?**

Different pure substances have different melting and boiling points. Most metals have a high melting point. This makes them solid at room temperature. But mercury is a metal with a low melting point. It is a liquid at room temperature.

Do mixtures have a fixed melting point?

A mixture is not pure because it is made of more than one substance. We can make a mixture of ice and salt and see what its melting point is.

Look at the pictures. They show that a mixture of ice and salt has a lower melting point than ice. The more salt there is, the lower the melting point. Mixtures do not have a fixed melting point.

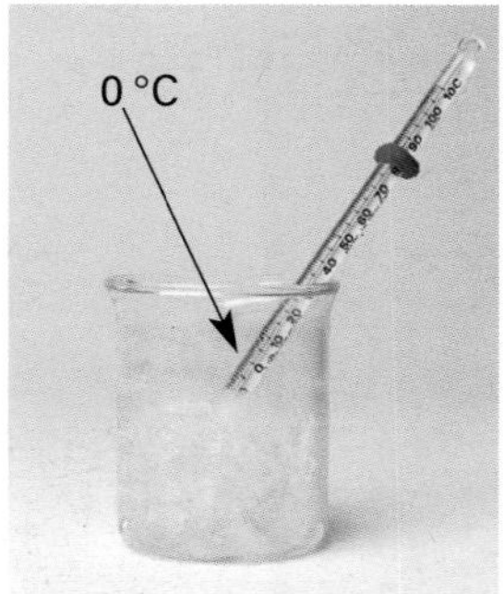

Pure ice melts at 0 °C.

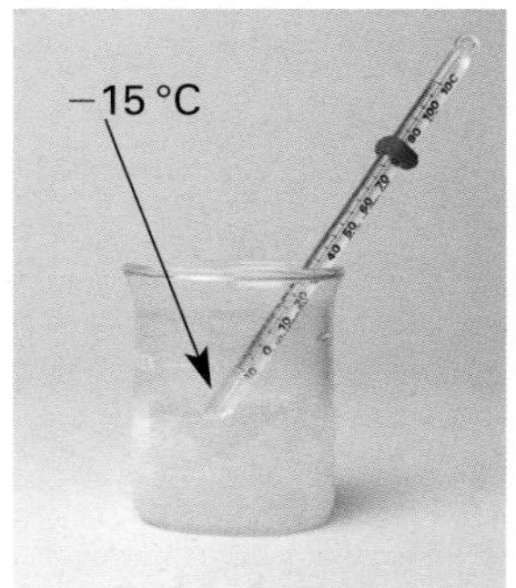

A mixture of ice and salt melts at −15 °C.

c Do mixtures have a fixed melting point?

Do mixtures have a fixed boiling point?

Look at the pictures. They show that a mixture of water and salt has a higher boiling point than water. The more salt there is, the higher the boiling point. Mixtures do not have a fixed boiling point.

d Do mixtures have a fixed boiling point?

Pure water boils at 100 °C.

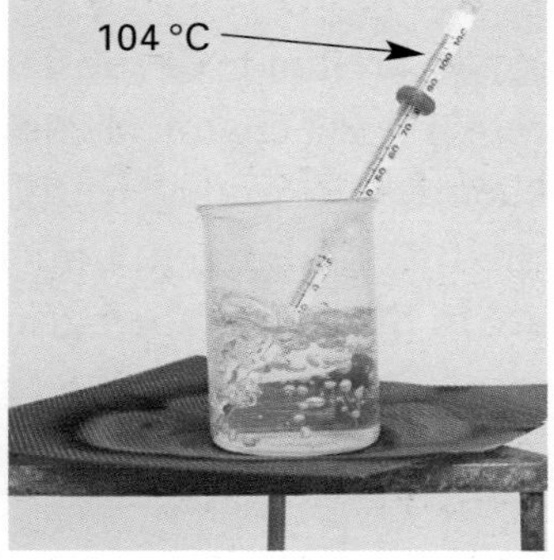

A mixture of salt and water boils at 104 °C.

QUESTIONS

Copy out these sentences, choosing the correct words:

Pure substances **have/do not have** fixed melting and boiling points.

Mixtures **have/do not have** fixed melting and boiling points.

KEY POINTS

- Pure substances have fixed melting and boiling points.
- Mixtures do not have fixed melting and boiling points.

G Rocks and weathering

G1 WHAT ARE ROCKS MADE OF?

What is a rock?

A rock is a solid, non-living material found in the ground. Scientists called **geologists** study rocks. To a geologist even sand is called a rock.

Sand

Sandstone

a What do we call a scientist who studies rocks?

What are rocks made of?

Rocks are made of substances called **minerals.** Each mineral is a chemical compound. It even has its own chemical formula. Nearly every type of rock is a mixture of different minerals. The minerals in the rock are in little bits called **grains**.

Look at the picture. You can see the grains in the rock. The grains fit together to make the rock.

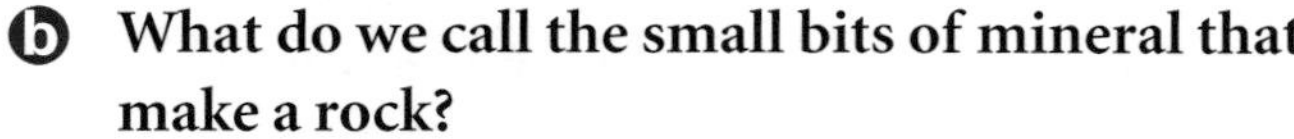

b What do we call the small bits of mineral that make a rock?

Sometimes the grains are so small that we need a microscope to see them.

What are the two main textures of rock?

The word **texture** usually means whether something is rough or smooth. Geologists use the word to describe how big the grains are, how they are joined together and whether they have spaces between them.

Look at the pictures. In some rocks the grains fit tightly together. In other rocks, the grains have spaces between them. This gives two different textures.

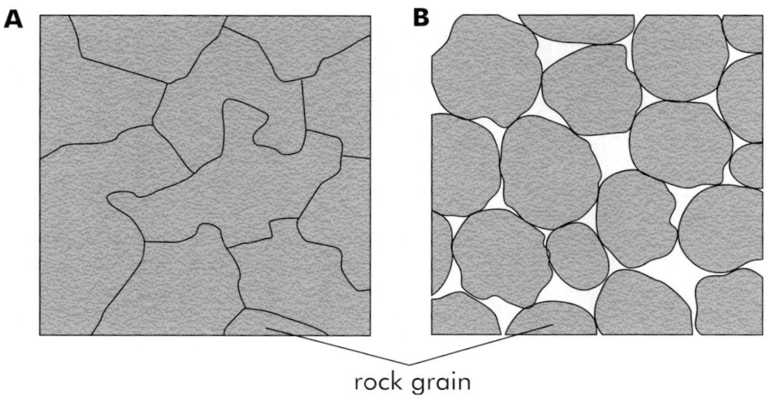

c **Draw a picture of the two different textures of rock. Label them correctly.**

What difference does the texture of a rock make?

If a rock has spaces between the grains, we say it is **porous**. We can tell if a rock is porous by putting it in water. If air bubbles come out of the rock it must be porous. The air was trapped in the spaces between the grains.

d **Where have the air bubbles come from?**

Sometimes these spaces in the rock can contain oil. Oil wells are drilled where the porous rocks contain oil. Non-porous rocks don't have spaces between the rock grains.

e **Where would you dig a well to find oil, in porous or non-porous rock?**

QUESTIONS

Copy these sentences and fill in the spaces using the words below:

grains minerals porous

A rock is a collection of ________ . The minerals are found in little bits called ________ . Some rocks are called ________ because they have spaces between the ________ .

KEY POINTS

- A rock is a mixture of minerals.
- Minerals are found in bits called grains.
- Some rocks have spaces between the grains. We call them porous rocks.

G2 WATER AND WEATHERING

What effect does water have on rocks?

Rocks get worn away. Look at the pictures of gravestones. They are both made from the same rock. One of them is about 80 years older than the other.

a **Which of the gravestones is older?**

One of the things that causes rocks to wear away is rainwater. Look at the picture of a cathedral. Rain has worn away the rock that it is made from.

How does rainwater affect rock?

Rainwater is **acidic**. As it falls through the air, gases dissolve in the water that make it acidic. Rainwater reacts with some minerals in rocks, but not others.

Look at the picture below. It shows some very strange rock shapes. These shapes have happened because the acidic rainwater has reacted with some of the minerals in the rock and not others. Some parts of the rock became weak and crumbled away.

b **Why do the rocks in the picture have such strange shapes?**

How do we get caves?

Limestone is a rock made from a mineral called **calcium carbonate**. Acidic rainwater reacts with calcium carbonate very easily. The rainwater seeps into cracks in the limestone. It reacts with the limestone, wearing it away until it leaves a cave. Some of the best caves in the world are in areas of limestone.

C Why are most caves found in limestone rocks?

Rainwater reacts chemically with rocks in other ways too. Rocks that contain iron can turn red when rain falls on them. Look at the picture. It shows rocks that have gone rusty.

What is weathering?

Weathering is a word that means rocks have changed. Rainwater causes **chemical weathering**. In chemical weathering, new substances are made.

QUESTIONS

Copy these sentences and fill in the spaces using the words below:

minerals   weathered   acidic

Rainwater is slightly ________ . It can react with the rock and dissolve some of the ________ in rock. Limestone is easily ________ by acidic rainwater.

KEY POINTS

- Rainwater is slightly acidic. It can dissolve some of the minerals in rocks, and react with others.
- Rainwater causes chemical weathering.

G3 TEMPERATURE AND WEATHERING

How does temperature affect rocks?

Look at the picture of the desert. We think of deserts as hot places. They are hot during the day. But at night the temperature can get close to freezing.

Look at the picture of the mountains. The temperature in the mountains can be just above freezing in the daytime but below freezing at night.

a Which environment above, the desert or the mountain, has the bigger change of temperature?

What does temperature do to rocks?

Weathering by heating and cooling

When a mineral gets hot, it gets bigger – it **expands**. When a mineral gets cold, it gets smaller – it **contracts**. The problem is that different minerals expand and contract by different amounts.

Deserts have very big changes in temperature. They are hot during the day and cold at night. This means different minerals in the rock will be expanding and contracting a lot. So the rock cracks and breaks into smaller pieces. This is why many deserts are full of small bits of rock called sand.

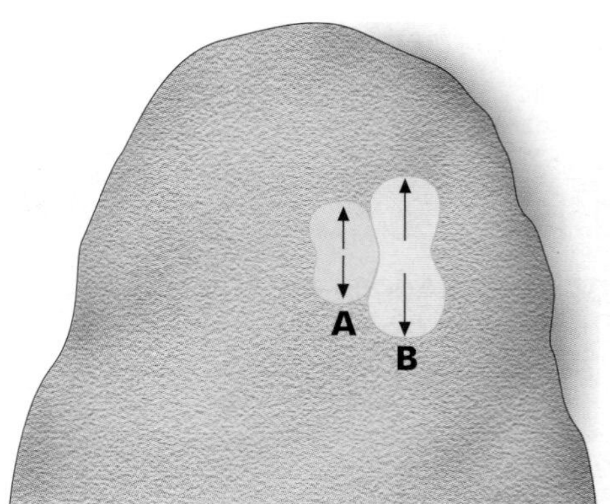

If mineral A expands more than mineral B, a crack may form.

b Why is a desert full of sand?

Weathering by freezing and thawing

When water freezes, it expands. This is why water pipes sometimes burst in the winter.

Water gets into small cracks in the rock. When the water freezes it expands. This makes the crack bigger.

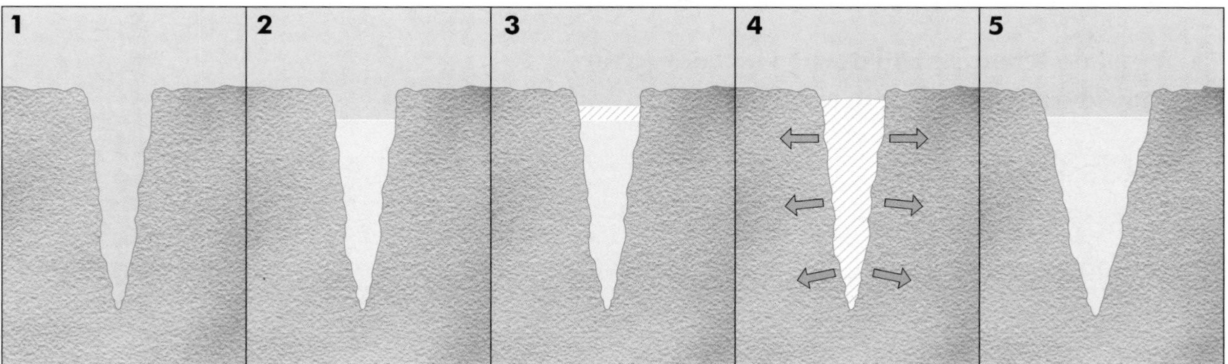

A crack in a rock... fills with water which... freezes over. All the water freezes and expands... widening the crack.

Each time the water freezes and thaws, the crack gets bigger and bigger. Eventually the rock falls apart. This is called **physical weathering**. No new materials are made. The rock just keeps being broken down into smaller pieces.

Look back again at the picture of the mountain. There are lots of small rocks. These rocks have broken off the mountain because the temperature there falls below freezing and rises again very often.

C **Why do some rocks break apart in very cold weather?**

QUESTIONS

Copy these sentences and fill in the spaces using the words below:

break contract expands

Different minerals expand and ________ differently. This causes rocks to ________ apart. When water freezes it ________ . This also causes rocks to ________ apart.

KEY POINTS

- Temperature causes rocks to weather by making them expand and contract.
- Temperature causes rocks to weather by water freezing in tiny cracks.

G4 TRANSPORT AND EROSION

What happens to the weathered bits of rock?

Weathering causes bits of rock to fall to the ground. But this isn't the end of the story. Eventually they get moved to somewhere else. Scientists call this **transport**.

ⓐ What do scientists call it when bits of rock are moved from one place to another?

What is transport?

Bits of rock can be transported in three ways:

1. Blown by the wind. The picture opposite shows grains of sand being blown in a sandstorm.

1

2. Washed along by water. Look at the picture below. This happens in rivers, and also in the sea.

2

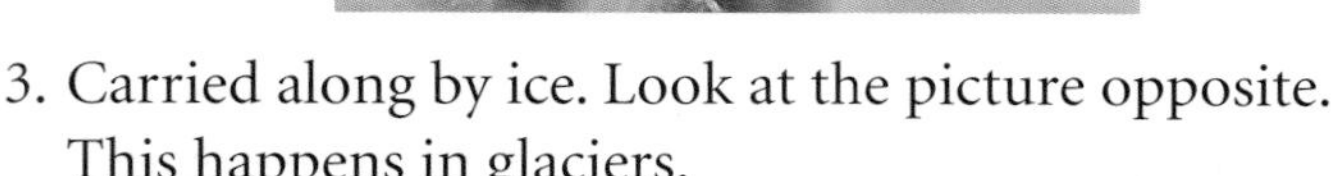

3. Carried along by ice. Look at the picture opposite. This happens in glaciers.

3

ⓑ Name three ways that bits of rock can be transported.

What happens during transport?

When rocks are transported they bump against one another. This does two things to the bits of rock:

- It makes them smaller.
- It knocks off the sharp edges and makes them rounded.

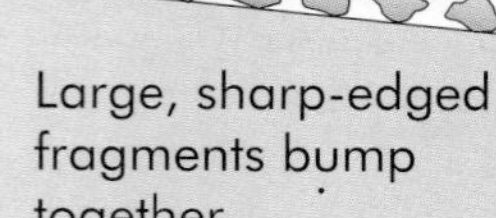
Large, sharp-edged fragments bump together . . .
knocking off corners . . .
and becoming smaller

We can nearly always tell when a rock has been transported. It will have rounded edges. Look at the two pictures of bits of rock in a river (picture **A**) and on a beach (picture **B**).

A

B

c **Which picture shows rocks that have been transported the furthest?**

Sometimes transported rocks don't have rounded edges. This only happens when they have been transported in ice. The ice keeps the rocks apart so they don't bump into each other.

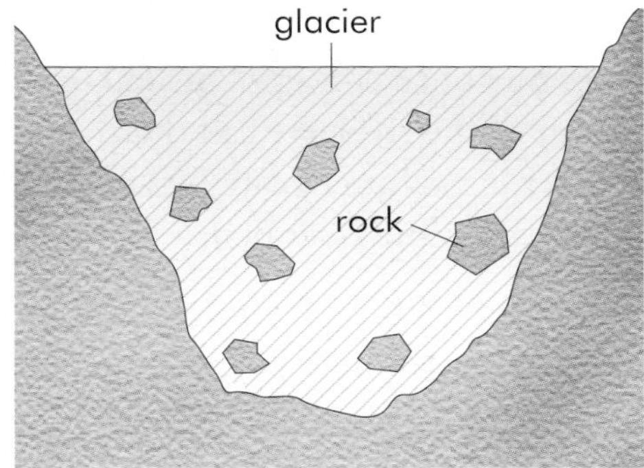

d **Why don't rocks transported by glaciers have rounded edges?**

QUESTIONS

Copy these sentences and fill in the spaces using the words below:

ice   rounded   transported

When rocks have been weathered, the bits that fall to the ground are usually ________ away. Rocks that have been transported by wind and water have ________ edges. Rocks that have been transported by ________ have sharper edges.

KEY POINTS

- Weathered bits of rock are usually transported.
- Rocks can be transported by wind, water and ice.

G5 WHAT HAPPENS WHEN TRANSPORT STOPS?

Grinding to a halt

When a river reaches a lake or the sea, it slows down. This means that it can no longer wash the bits of rock along. They sink to the bottom of the river bed. Fast-flowing water can carry particles of all sizes. Slow-flowing water can carry only small particles.

The same thing happens with the wind. When the wind slows down, the grains of rock fall to the ground. We call this process **deposition**.

a **What happens to the bits of rock when the river slows down?**

b **As the river slows down, which bits of rock will be deposited first, the big heavy ones or the small light ones?**

Deposition

When bits of rock fragments fall to the bottom of the river, we call them **sediments**. Sediments are bits of rock deposited on the river bed.

Look at the picture. It shows sediments deposited by the Yellow River.

c **What do we call material deposited by a river as it slows down?**

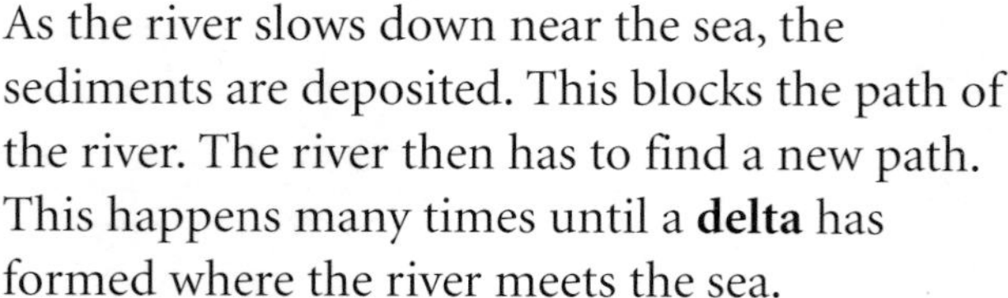

As the river slows down near the sea, the sediments are deposited. This blocks the path of the river. The river then has to find a new path. This happens many times until a **delta** has formed where the river meets the sea.

Look at the picture. It was taken from a space shuttle. It shows a delta being formed.

What is deposited where?

Look at the picture. It shows what is deposited where.

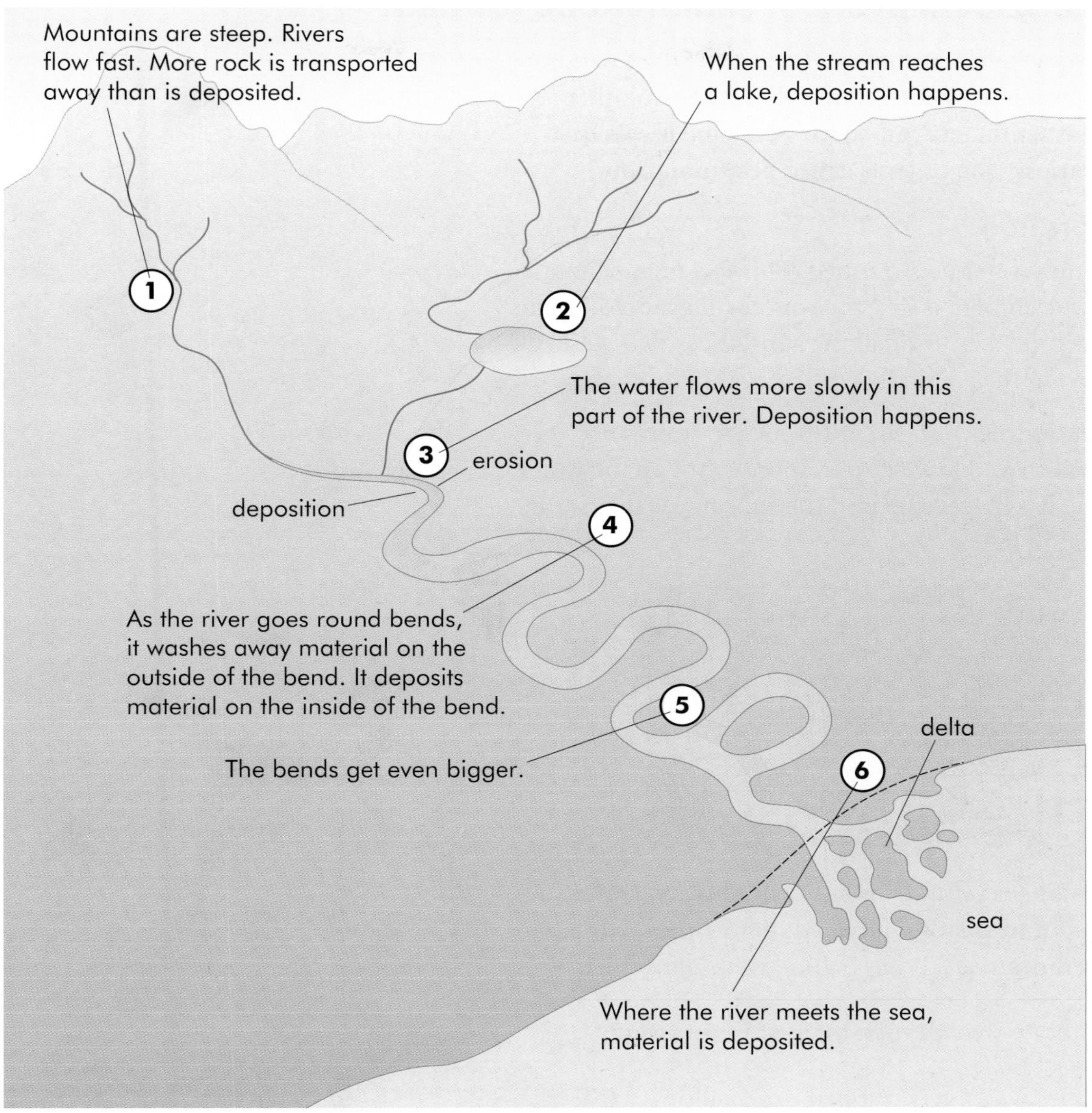

Mountains are steep. Rivers flow fast. More rock is transported away than is deposited.
When the stream reaches a lake, deposition happens.
1
2
The water flows more slowly in this part of the river. Deposition happens.
3
erosion
deposition
4
As the river goes round bends, it washes away material on the outside of the bend. It deposits material on the inside of the bend.
5
The bends get even bigger.
delta
6
sea
Where the river meets the sea, material is deposited.

QUESTIONS

Copy these sentences and fill in the spaces using the words below:

first last deposited

When a river slows down, sediments are ________. Larger bits are deposited ________ and smaller bits are deposited ________.

KEY POINTS

- When transport stops, rock fragments are deposited as sediment.
- Larger rocks are deposited first. Smaller bits are deposited last.

G6 HOW DO SEDIMENTS FORM LAYERS?

How else can layers of sediment be formed?

You have seen how sediments can form when wind or moving water slows down. But there are two other ways that sediments can be formed. One is called **evaporation**. The other is called **accumulation**.

Evaporation

Sometimes water gets trapped. This can happen in a lake. If the climate is dry, the water will evaporate. This leaves behind a layer of all the substances that were dissolved in the water. It is called **evaporite rock.**

You can try this yourself. Put some tap water in a shallow dish and leave it to evaporate. When the water has gone it will leave behind the substances that were dissolved in it.

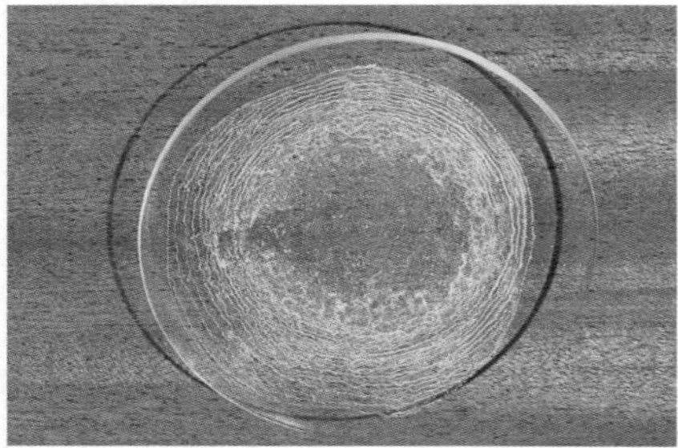

Just imagine how much is left behind when a whole lake evaporates. This happened many times to the Mediterranean Sea. It left behind rock 2 km thick.

a What do we call rock formed in this way?

Sometimes water gets trapped in a shallow tropical lagoon. It is cut off from the ocean by coral reefs. As the water evaporates the minerals dissolved in the sea water sink to the bottom. Because more sea water enters the lagoon, the process can continue for millions of years. This can build up very thick layers of evaporite rock.

Accumulation

Sediments may also form by the accumulation of dead organisms. Look at the picture. It shows microscopic sea creatures. Each of them is surrounded by a tiny shell. When they die, the shells fall to the bottom of the sea. Over millions of years the shells pile up on top of one another. In time they turn into rocks like chalk and other limestones.

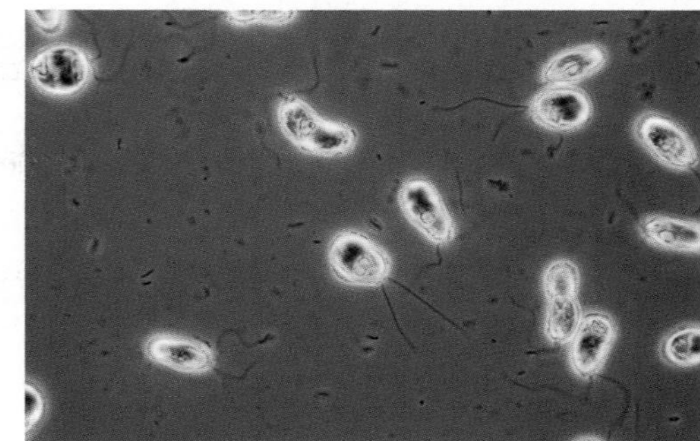

The rocks are laid down in layers

The sediments are laid down in layers. When they turn into rock the layers are still there. Younger rock is formed on top of older rock.

Look at the picture. It shows the rock at a cliff face. This rock was formed over millions of years under the sea. You can still see the layers in the rock.

(b) Which layer do you think was formed first, A or B?

The layers form a historical record over millions of years. Geologists can look at **fossils** trapped in the rock. This tells them what conditions were like millions of years ago.

Fossils are a cast of where a dead animal or plant was squashed or the remains of it left after millions of years. The kinds of fossils also tell geologists how old one rock is compared with another.

QUESTIONS

Copy these sentences and fill in the spaces using the words below:

bed   evaporates   shells

Rocks are formed when trapped water ________ . Rocks like limestone and chalk are formed when the ________ of small creatures accumulate on the sea ________ .

KEY POINTS

- Rocks can form when a trapped lake evaporates.
- Rocks can form when shells from small sea creatures accumulate on the sea bed.

H The rock cycle

H1 MAKING SEDIMENTARY ROCKS

How are sedimentary rocks formed?

In Unit 8G you saw how sediments can form layers. We are now going to look at how these layers turn into rock. Making rocks from sediments takes millions of years.

1. At first a sediment is **deposited**. Look at the picture. It shows a sediment of pebbles.
2. As more sediments build up, the weight squashes the ones underneath and puts them under pressure. This is called **compaction**. The sediment heats up as it is squashed.
3. The water is squeezed out. Other minerals that were dissolved in the water are left behind. They act like glue and stick the sediment together. This is called **cementation**.
4. After millions of years, rock is formed. Rocks formed like this are called **sedimentary rocks**.

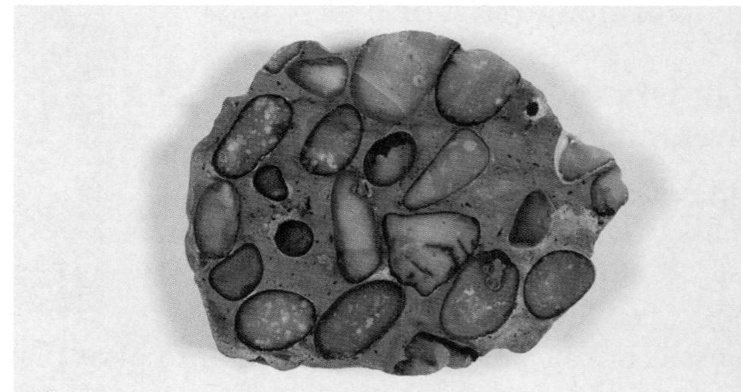

Sedimentary rock formed from pebbles

a **What do we call rocks that are formed from sediments?**

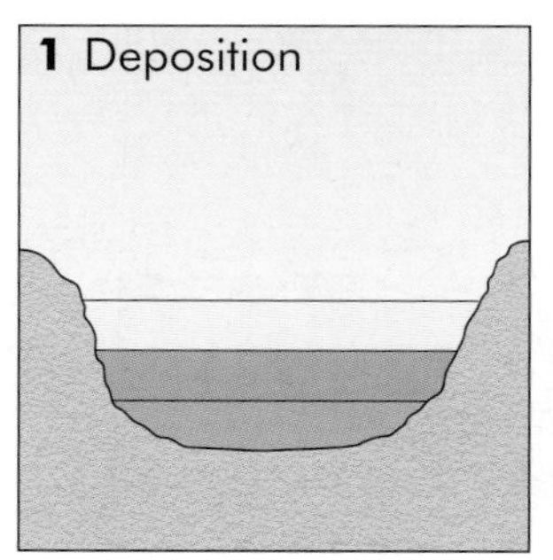

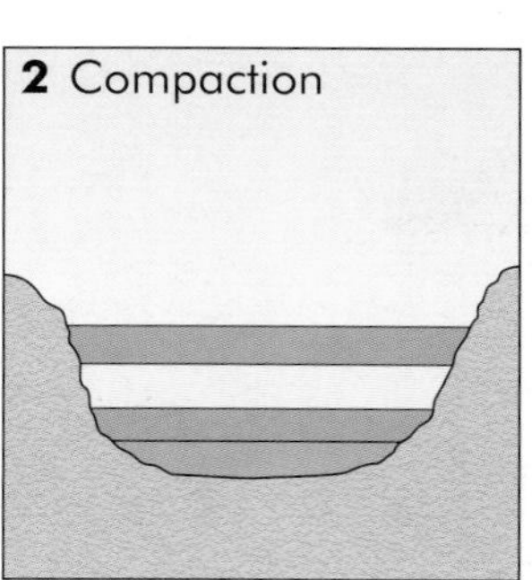

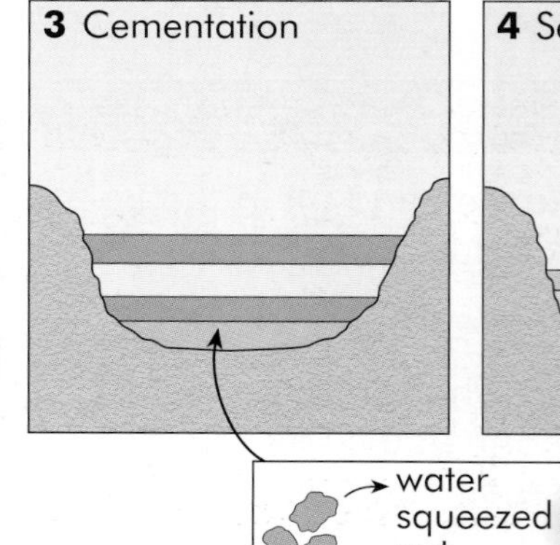

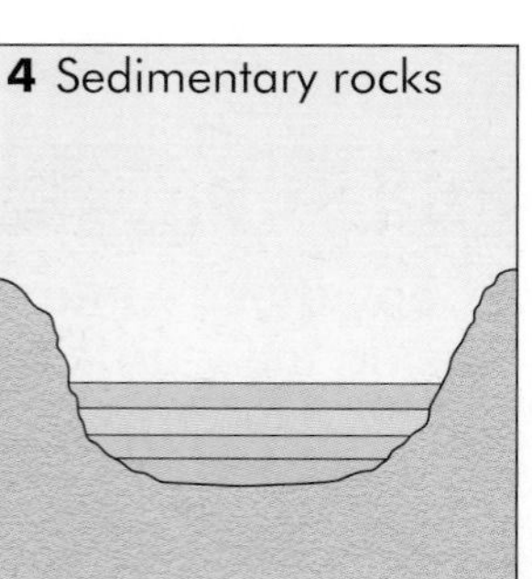

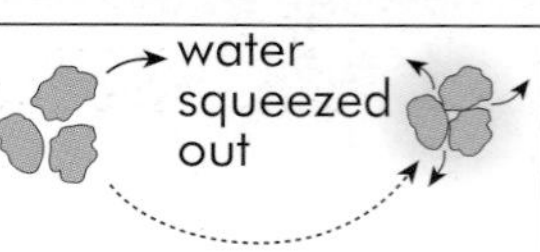

What do sedimentary rocks look like?

Here are some clues that will help you identify sedimentary rocks.

Sedimentary rocks:

- have **grains**, not crystals, held together by a natural **cement**
- are sometimes **porous** and have air spaces between the grains
- often contain **fossils**.

(b) How would you identify a sedimentary rock?

Examples of sedimentary rocks

Sandstone is made from tiny grains of quartz cemented together.

Limestone is made from the shells of dead sea creatures. This one contains fossils.

Shale is formed from squashed mud.

(c) Name three different sedimentary rocks.

QUESTIONS

Copy these sentences and fill in the spaces using the words below:

compacted   fossils   grains   cemented

Sedimentary rocks are formed when sediments are ________ and then ________ . The rocks have ________ that are cemented together. They also often contain ________ .

KEY POINTS

- Sedimentary rocks are formed when sediments are squashed and cemented under pressure.
- Examples of sedimentary rocks include sandstone, limestone and shale.

H2 ARE ALL LIMESTONES THE SAME?

What is limestone made of?

Limestone is one type of sedimentary rock. But it can be formed in many different ways. So there are lots of different kinds of limestone, with many different colours.

Limestone is usually made out of a mineral called **calcium carbonate**. The amount of calcium carbonate and other minerals can vary. It depends on how the limestone was formed.

a What mineral is limestone usually made from?

Different kinds of limestone

Some limestone contains fossils.

Stalactites and stalagmites in caves are made of limestone.

Chalk is a type of limestone which isn't usually very hard.

Bits of shell and coral can turn into limestone.

Look at the picture. This is called oolitic limestone. It is made when limestone is deposited on grains of sand. The waves roll them across the sea floor. They get worn into a round shape.

(b) Name two different kinds of limestone.

How much carbonate is there in limestone?

In Year 7 you learnt that carbonates react with acid. Geologists use this to test for limestone.

- They crush the rock to a powder.
- Then they add acid.
- The mixture fizzes as carbon dioxide is given off.
- They weigh the mixture before and afterwards.
- They can then work out the mass of carbon dioxide given off.
- The more carbon dioxide, the more carbonate was in the rock.

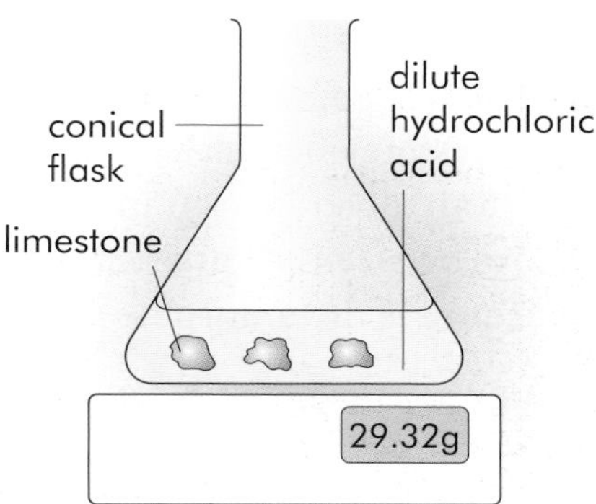

(c) Joey tested two similar sized limestone rocks with acid. Rock A gave off more carbon dioxide than rock B. Which rock has more carbonate, A or B?

QUESTIONS

Copy these sentences, choosing the correct words:

Limestone **contains/does not contain** calcium carbonate.

Calcium carbonate **reacts/does not react** with acid to produce carbon dioxide.

KEY POINTS

- There are many different kinds of limestone, made in different ways.
- Limestone contains calcium carbonate.

H3 METAMORPHIC ROCKS

What is a metamorphic rock?

Metamorphic rocks are made from other rocks. Sedimentary rocks are changed into metamorphic rocks by heat and high pressure. This happens deep inside the Earth.

How are metamorphic rocks formed?

This is what happens deep inside the Earth.

- Sedimentary rocks are squashed under other rocks.
- This makes the rocks heat up.
- The heat changes minerals into different minerals.
- The heat and pressure destroy many of the fossils in the sedimentary rock.
- The heat changes minerals into different minerals.
- The pressure often makes the crystals line up in bands.
- There are no grains left in the new rock, so any spaces between the grains will have disappeared. This means metamorphic rocks are not porous.

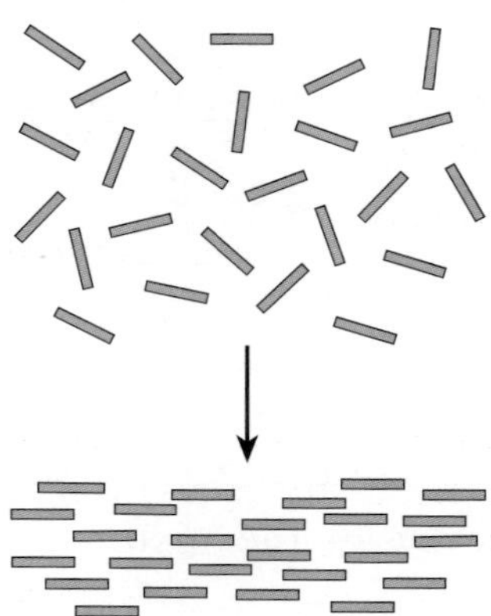

When the rock is squeezed, the crystals often line up in bands.

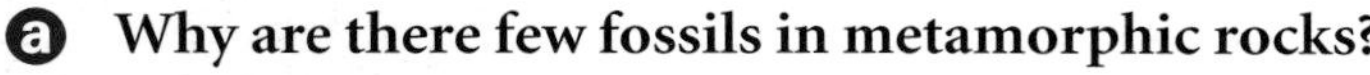

a **Why are there few fossils in metamorphic rocks?**

b **Why are metamorphic rocks not porous?**

What are metamorphic rocks formed from?

The type of metamorphic rock formed depends on what rock it was made from, and on how much heat and/or pressure there was.

When limestone is heated inside the Earth, it turns into marble.

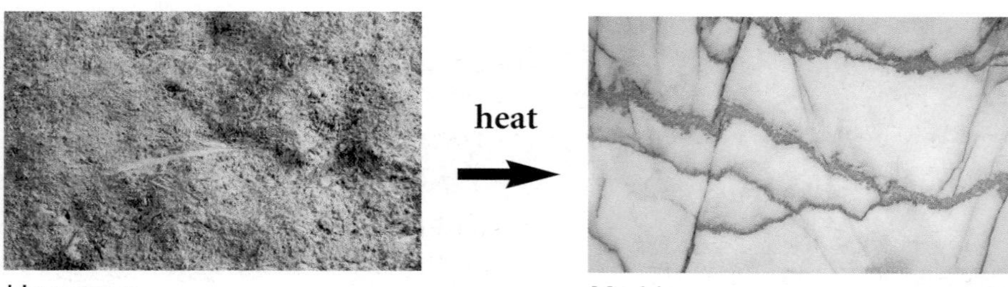

Limestone

Marble

c **What kind of sedimentary rock is marble made from?**

d **How is marble made?**

When mudstone is heated under high pressure, it turns into slate.

Shale (mudstone)

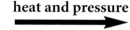

heat and pressure

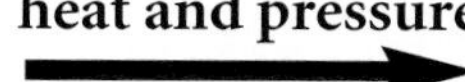

Slate

e Which of the two rocks shown above is a metamorphic rock?

This is not the end of the story for slate. Slate can be heated to a higher temperature and put under higher pressure. If this happens it will change again into other kinds of rock.

Slate

heat and pressure

Schist

very high temperature and pressure

Gneiss

QUESTIONS

Copy these sentences and fill in the spaces using the words below:

marble sedimentary temperature

Metamorphic rocks may be made from ________ rocks. This happens when there is high ________ and pressure. An example is when limestone is changed into ________ .

KEY POINTS

- Metamorphic rocks are made from other rocks.
- This happens when the rocks are heated and/or put under higher pressure.

H4 MAKING IGNEOUS ROCKS

How are igneous rocks formed?

Igneous rocks are formed from other rocks that have melted. It takes a very high temperature to melt a rock. Inside the Earth it is very hot. The rock melts to form **magma**. Magma is a hot, sticky liquid that can flow.

(a) What do we call a rock that has melted?

Magma turns back into solid rock in two different ways.

1. The magma is squirted out of the Earth. This sometimes happens under the sea. It sometimes comes out of volcanoes. It cools very quickly and turns back into solid rock.

2. The magma cools slowly under the ground. It may be millions of years before it reaches the Earth's surface as an outcrop of rock.

This igneous rock was formed deep underground.

How do crystals form in rocks?

When magma cools into solid rock, crystals form.

Sometimes these crystals are big and we can see them easily. Look at the picture. You can see the crystals in a rock called **granite**. Granite is an igneous rock.

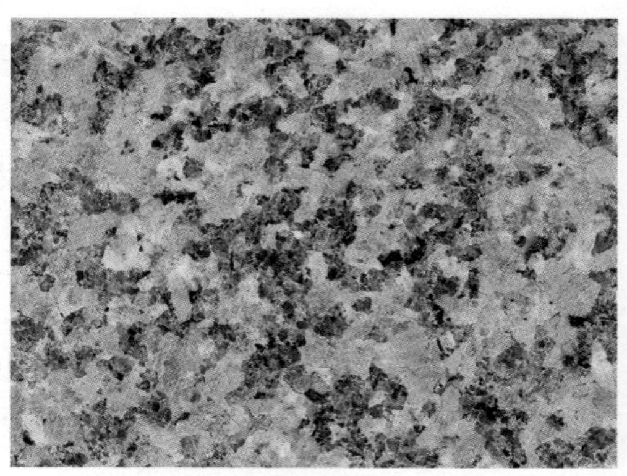

(b) Name an igneous rock that has large crystals.

Sometimes the crystals are very small. It is much more difficult to see them. Look at the picture. Most of the crystals are too small to see. The rock is called **basalt**.

c Name an igneous rock that has very small crystals.

Different igneous rocks also have different colours. This is because they contain different minerals. Basalt contains lots of iron minerals. This is why it is darker than granite.

Why are some crystals big and some crystals small?

The size of the crystals depends on how quickly the rock cools.

- The slower it cools, the bigger the crystals.
- The quicker it cools, the smaller the crystals.

Granite has big crystals. This means it cooled very slowly. It took millions of years. This is because granite forms deep inside the Earth.

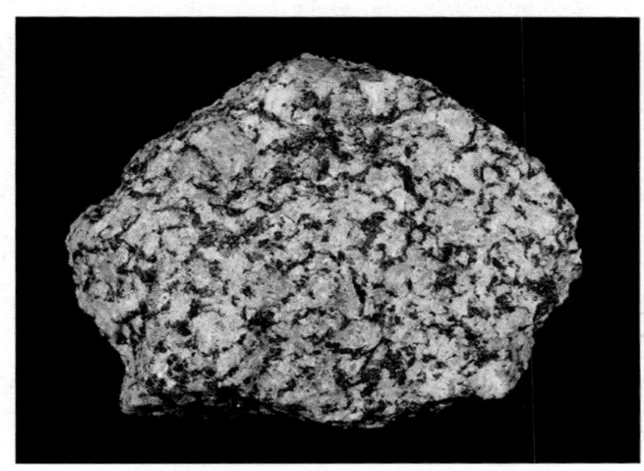

Basalt has small crystals. This means it cooled very quickly. It took hours or weeks. This is because it was squirted from the Earth into cold sea water or cool air.

d Look at the picture of an igneous rock. Did it cool more quickly or more slowly than basalt?

QUESTIONS

Copy these sentences, choosing the correct words:

Granite has **big/small** crystals. This means it cooled **quickly/slowly**.

Basalt has **big/small** crystals. This means it cooled **quickly/slowly**.

KEY POINTS

- Igneous rocks that cool slowly have large crystals, such as granite.
- Igneous rocks that cool quickly have small crystals, such as basalt.

H5 HOW CAN WE COMPARE IGNEOUS ROCKS?

Some rocks are 'heavier'

Some types of rock feel 'heavier' in our hands than other types of rock of about the same size. This is true for many types of igneous rocks.

We want to compare how 'heavy' two different types of igneous rock are. To make a fair test, we should compare two pieces of rock of exactly the same size.

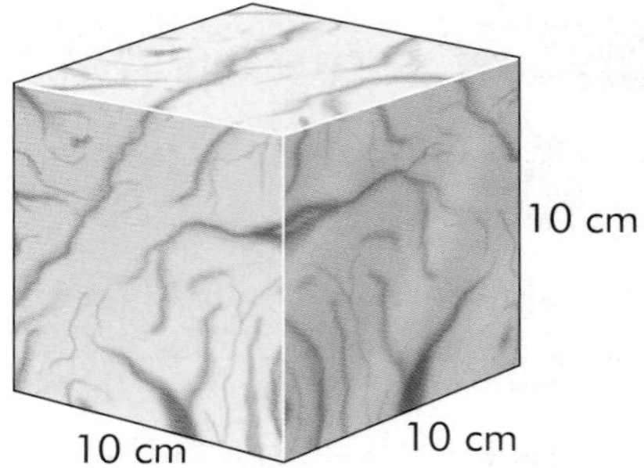

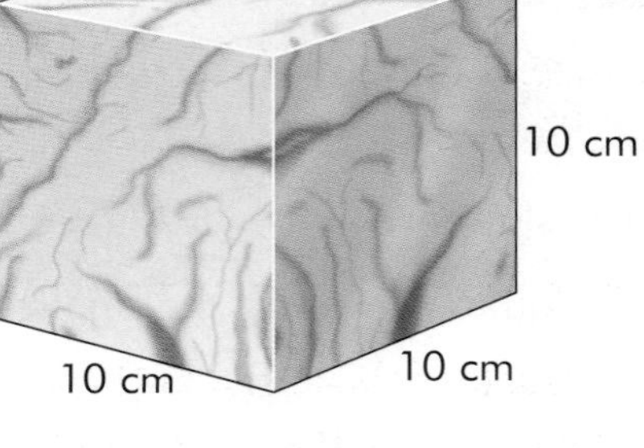

a Why should we compare two equal sized pieces of rock?

Rocks do not often come in pieces of equal size. It would not be easy to cut two rocks, basalt and granite, into two equal sized pieces like the block in the picture.

But there is a way we can compare them. We can use different sized pieces of two different rocks as long as we know their mass and their volume.

How do we measure the mass of rocks?

We can find the mass in grams of two pieces of rock using a balance, as shown opposite.

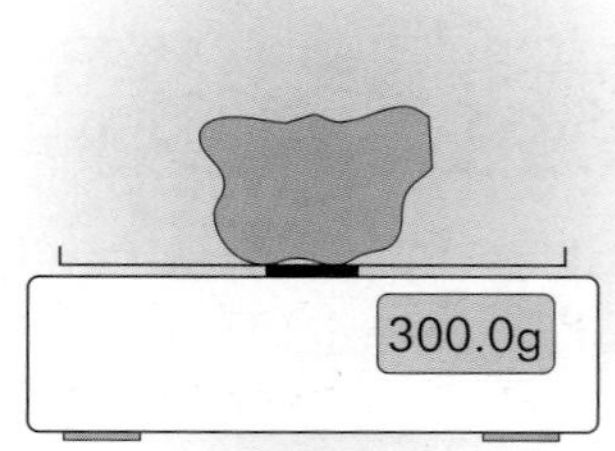

How do we measure the volume of rocks?

Measuring the volume of two pieces of rock is a little more messy. We need to use a Eureka beaker. This is named after Archimedes, who shouted 'Eureka!' when he discovered how to do it.

When we put a piece of rock in the beaker, the amount (volume) of water that flows out of the spout is the same as the volume of the piece of rock. To find the volume of the rock, all we have to do is measure the volume of the water that flows from the spout.

How do we compare the density of rocks?

If we now divide the mass of a rock by its volume, we get a number called the rock's **density**. It does not matter how big or small the rock is. We can compare the density of one rock with the density of another rock, whatever its size.

$$\text{density} = \frac{\text{mass}}{\text{volume}}$$

Look at the table. It shows the mass and volume of two types of rock. The small piece of rock is more dense than the large piece of rock.

Picture	Size	Volume	Mass	Mass ÷ volume	Density
	large	300	600	$\frac{600}{300}$	2
	small	100	300	$\frac{300}{100}$	3

b Which of the rocks in the table is more dense, the large one or the small one?

Why are 'heavy' rocks heavy?

Some igneous rocks contain minerals that are 'heavier' or more dense than others. The density of the rock depends on the minerals that are in it. Minerals that contain iron tend to be very dense. Some igneous rocks contain a lot of iron minerals. Granite contains less iron than basalt so it is less dense.

QUESTIONS

Copy these sentences and fill in the spaces using the words below:

compare density volume

We can find the ________ of a rock by dividing its mass by its ________. When we know the density we can ________ one rock with another.

KEY POINTS

- We can compare igneous rocks by looking at how dense they are.

H6 THE ROCK CYCLE

What is the rock cycle?

You now know that:

- sedimentary rocks are formed from the weathered remains of other rocks
- metamorphic rocks are formed from other rocks that have been squashed and heated a lot
- igneous rocks are formed from other rocks that have melted.

The **rock cycle** is a way of linking together all these processes. It shows how rocks on the Earth are slowly being changed from one type to the next.

It's all one big system

Look at the picture. It shows the rock cycle. The blue colour at the top of the picture shows where it is cooler near the Earth's surface. The red colour at the bottom of the picture shows where it is hot deep inside the Earth.

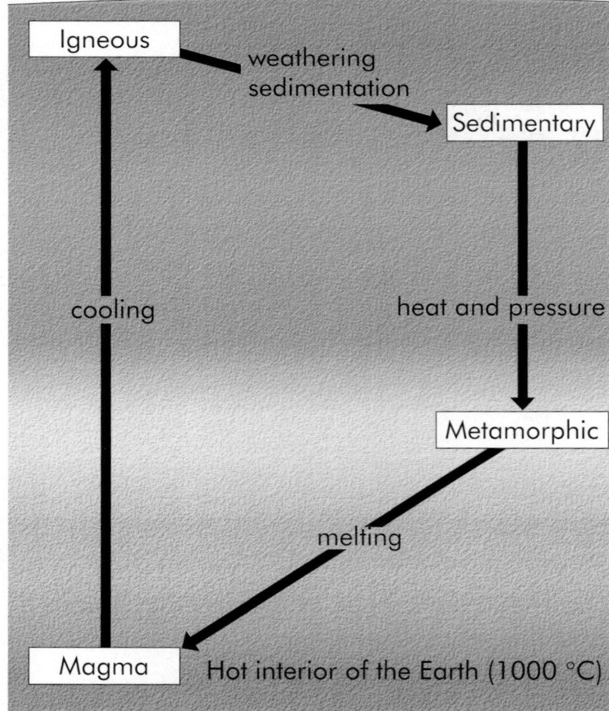

a **Look at the picture. What type of rock is igneous rock made from?**

b **What type of rock is metamorphic rock made from?**

How long does it all take?

The rock cycle can take many millions of years. It is hard for us to imagine such a long time. We are only on the Earth for less than a hundred years.

Some processes in the rock cycle take millions of years. This is how long some sedimentary rocks take to form. Other processes may take as little as days or weeks. A volcano can erupt in a day.

So to us, some rocks may not appear to change very much. It's a bit like looking at one frame in a film and trying to work out what the story of the film is all about.

Look at the film strip below. Can you work out the story from one frame? You need all of the frames to tell the complete story.

C **Why is it hard for us to imagine what happens in the rock cycle?**

QUESTIONS

Copy these sentences and fill in the spaces using the words below:

cycle few millions rock

The rock ________ shows us how all the different kinds of ________ are formed. Parts of the rock cycle take place over ________ of years. In our lifetime we will see very ________ of the changes to the rocks.

KEY POINTS

- The rock cycle shows us how all the different kinds of rock are formed.
- It is hard to imagine because it takes place over such a long period of time.

I1 WHAT'S THE TEMPERATURE?

How hot does it feel?

How hot or cold something is is called its **temperature**. We are not very good at guessing temperature.

Look at the students in the picture. The boy is cold, so the water feels hot. The girl is hot, so the water feels cold. We obviously need a better way of measuring temperature that everybody will understand.

ahh . . .
hot!!
that's so
cool!!
10 °C

How do we measure temperature?

We use a **thermometer** to measure how hot things are. The units we use to measure temperature are **degrees Celsius**. We write this as °C for short.

Look at the picture. It shows what happens at different temperatures.

ⓐ **What is the normal temperature of your body?**

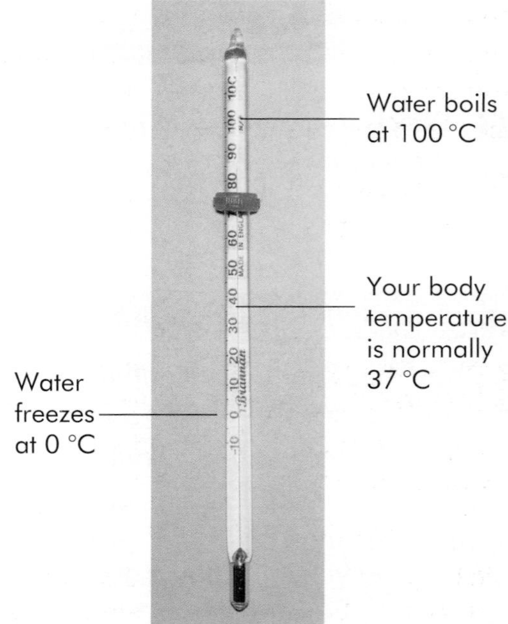
Water boils
at 100 °C
Your body
temperature
is normally
37 °C
Water
freezes
at 0 °C

The rubber bit near the top stops the thermometer rolling when you put it down.

Measuring different temperatures

Your **body temperature** is normally 37 °C. When you are ill it changes slightly. A doctor uses a clinical thermometer to check what your temperature is.

Clinical thermometers measure only from about 35 to 45 °C. This makes them much more accurate.

b **Why do clinical thermometers measure only a very small range?**

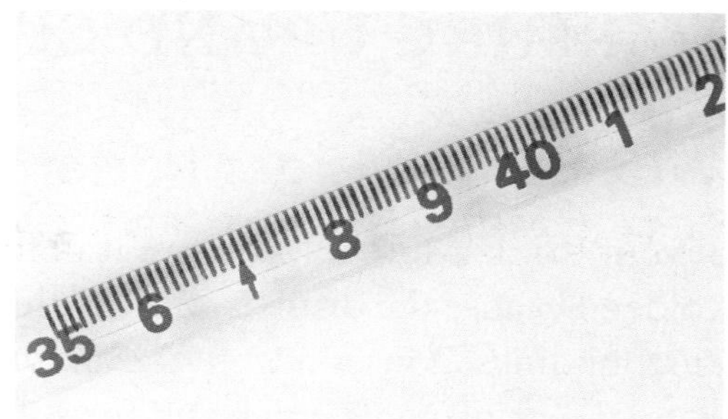

Clinical thermometer

If you wanted to measure the temperature of water boiling or freezing, you would need a thermometer with a bigger range. We use stirring thermometers at school which can measure from –10 to 110 °C.

Sometimes even this is not a big enough range. The temperature of the Sun is over 1 000 000 °C. But the temperature of the planet Pluto is –230 °C. That is a very big range.

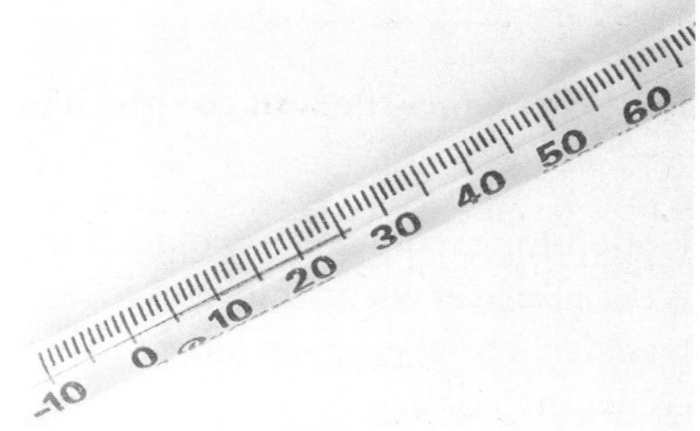

Stirring thermometer

How does a thermometer work?

Thermometers contain a liquid. When the liquid gets hot, it **expands** and moves up the tube. When the liquid gets cold, it **contracts** and moves down the tube. You can read the temperature off the thermometer at the top of the liquid level.

c **Why does the liquid go up the thermometer when it gets hot?**

QUESTIONS

Copy these sentences and fill in the spaces using the words below:

accurately   range   thermometer

We use a ________ to measure temperature ________. Some thermometers have a bigger ________ than others.

KEY POINTS

- We use a thermometer to measure temperature accurately.

12 WARMING UP AND COOLING DOWN

Why do things get hotter or colder?

If your drink is too hot, you can wait for it to get colder. Because the drink is warmer than its surroundings, it loses heat to the air and table around it. So the drink cools down and the surroundings warm up. This happens until they are both at the same temperature.

a Where does the heat go from a hot cup of tea?

Hotter things cool down. Colder things warm up. This is because heat energy moves. We call this an **energy transfer**. The energy spreads from hotter materials to cooler materials.

Scientists call heat energy **thermal energy**. The picture below shows where the thermal energy goes to from the hot cup of tea.

b What do scientists call heat energy?

Look at the table. It shows how quickly the cup of tea cooled down. The hotter the tea is, the faster the heat energy is transferred to the surroundings. When the temperature of the cup of tea and the surroundings is nearly the same, heat is transferred slowly.

c When does the cup of tea lose most of its heat energy?

Time (min)	Temperature (°C)
0	90
1	87
2	85
3	83
4	81
5	79
6	77
7	76
8	74
9	73
10	72

What does heat energy do?

All materials are made up of particles. When you give a material more heat energy, the particles move faster.

Look at the diagram. It shows what happens to the particles as they get more heat energy.

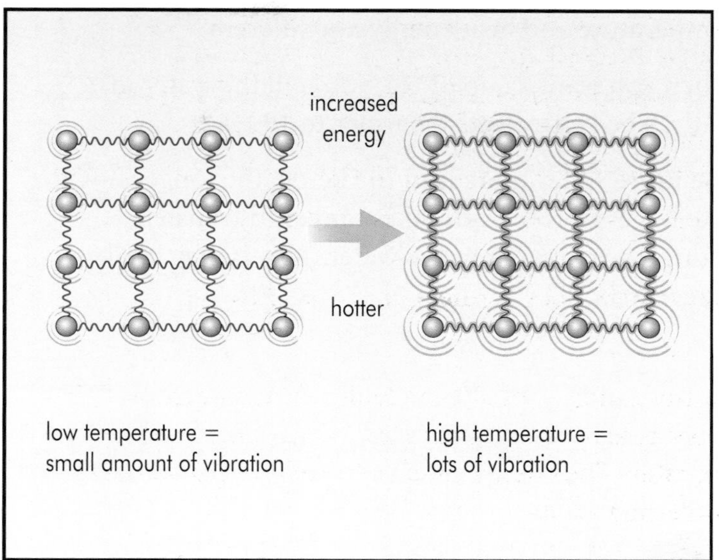

d What happens to the particles as they get more heat energy?

As the particles move faster, their temperature increases. The faster the particles move, the higher their temperature.

e What has happened to the temperature of the material when the particles move faster?

When the material cools down, the particles move more slowly.

f What has happened to the temperature when the particles move more slowly?

QUESTIONS

Copy these sentences, choosing the correct words:

Heat energy makes particles in a material move more **quickly/slowly**. When the particles move more **quickly/slowly**, the temperature rises.

Energy **can/cannot** move from one place to another. When there is a big temperature difference, energy is transferred more **quickly/slowly**.

KEY POINTS

- Heat energy makes particles in a material move more quickly.
- When particles move more quickly, the temperature increases.
- The bigger the temperature difference, the quicker heat is transferred.

13 TEMPERATURE AND HEAT ENERGY

How are temperature and heat energy different?

Temperature and heat energy are different.

When you want a cup of tea, you boil the water in a kettle. The kettle heats the water to 100 °C.

The more water there is in the kettle, the longer it will take to get to 100 °C. It takes longer to transfer enough heat energy to the water. This is why it takes longer to boil.

A small amount of water boils quickly.

A full kettle takes a longer time to boil.

a **Which will boil first, a kettle full of water or a kettle half full of water?**

b **Why does the full kettle take longer to boil?**

How much heat does it take?

We have seen that different amounts of water need different amounts of heat energy to heat them to the same temperature. But what about different materials?

To find out, we need to do a fair test. This means we need to use the same mass of each material. If we compare water with aluminium, it is no good having a small mass of water and a large mass of aluminium. They must both have the same mass.

c **If we compare two different materials, why should they both have the same mass?**

Imagine we put some heat energy into a 1 kg block of aluminium. The temperature of the aluminium rises by 10 °C.

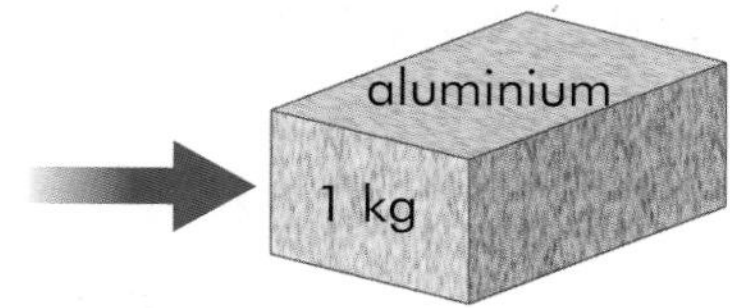

Now we put the same amount of heat into 1 kg of water. The temperature of the water rises by 2 °C.

d Using the same amount of heat, does the temperature of water or aluminium rise more?

Different materials need different amounts of heat energy to increase their temperature by the same amount.

Why does the temperature of aluminium rise more?

Particles of aluminium need less heat energy to make them vibrate. So when you heat the aluminium they vibrate much more quickly. The temperature of the aluminium rises a lot.

Particles of water need more energy to make them vibrate. So when you heat the water they vibrate more quickly, but not as quickly as aluminium. The temperature of the water rises less.

This means that if you put the same amount of heat energy into the same amount of aluminium and water, the aluminium will get hotter.

QUESTIONS

Copy these sentences, choosing the correct words:

Large amounts of material need **more/less** energy to warm up to the same temperature than small amounts of material. Different materials need **the same amount/different amounts** of heat energy to warm up to the same temperature.

KEY POINTS

- Temperature and heat energy are different. Large amounts of material need more heat energy to warm up to the same temperature than small amounts of material.
- Different materials need different amounts of heat energy to warm up to the same temperature.

14 WHAT ARE CONDUCTORS AND INSULATORS?

Why does the handle get hot?

When we use a metal saucepan, the handle can get very hot. Heat energy from the pan is transferred from the pan along the handle. This is called **conduction**. It happens even when the handle is not close to the flames.

We call materials that transfer heat energy like this **conductors**.

a What do we call materials that are good at transferring heat energy?

Metals often feel cold when we touch them. This is because they are transferring heat away from our fingers. This happens because metals are good conductors.

b Why do metals often feel cold when we touch them?

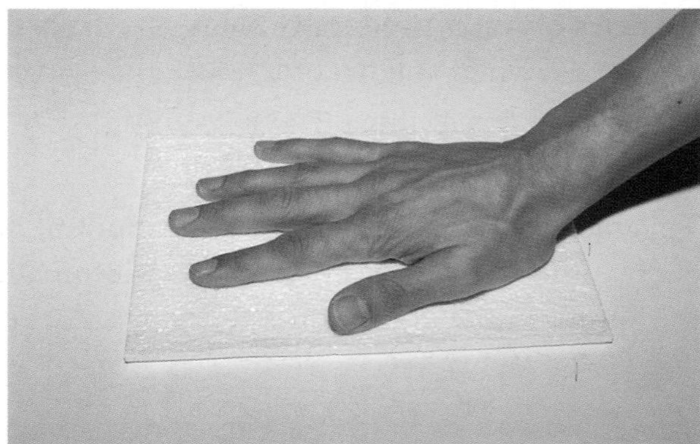

Some materials feel warm when we touch them. Look at the picture. It shows a hand touching polystyrene. Polystyrene feels warm when you touch it. This is because polystyrene is a poor conductor. The heat from your hand is not transferred away. It stays close to your hand in the polystyrene.

We call poor conductors **insulators**.

c Why does polystyrene feel warm when we touch it?

How do metals conduct heat energy?

Imagine the metal particles of the saucepan handle are like tennis balls. The tennis balls are held together by springs. The balls cannot move out of position. But they can vibrate.

Look at the picture. If you shake the ball on the left from side to side, the vibrations will be passed on to the balls around it. As these balls vibrate they will pass the vibrations on to the balls next to them. The more you shake the ball on the left, the more the vibrations get passed on.

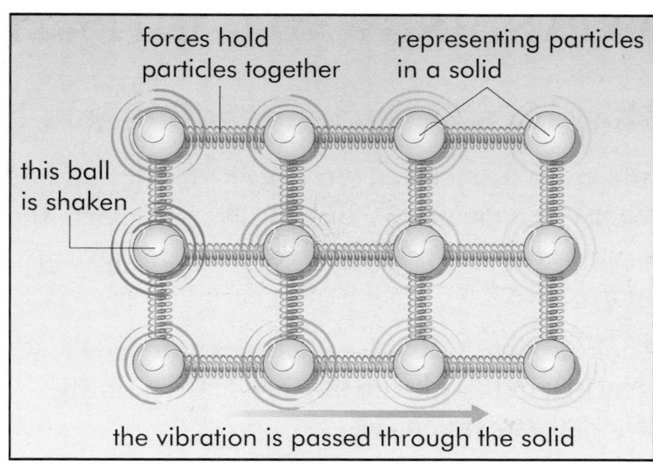
forces hold particles together
representing particles in a solid
this ball is shaken
the vibration is passed through the solid

Heat energy is transferred from particle to particle in a solid in a similar way. Even though the handle of the saucepan is away from the flames, it eventually gets hot. The particles all the way along the handle vibrate.

How do we keep warm?

Air is a good insulator.

Birds fluff up their feathers to trap air to keep warm.

Gardeners use bubble wrap in their greenhouses. The bubbles contain air which keeps in the heat during the cold winter.

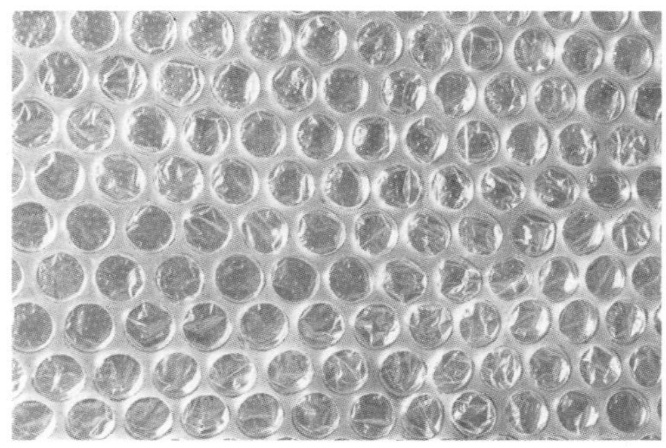

QUESTIONS

Copy these sentences and fill in the spaces using the words below:

conductors good insulators poor

Materials that transfer heat are called ________ . Materials that do not transfer heat are called ________ . Metal is a ________ conductor. Polystyrene is a ________ conductor.

KEY POINTS

- Materials that transfer heat are called conductors.
- Materials that do not transfer heat are called insulators.

15 EXPANDING AND CONTRACTING

How do solids change when you heat them?

You know that a metal gets bigger when it is heated. We say that the metal **expands**. The particles in the metal bar do not get any bigger. They just take up more space.

Look at the picture below. It shows four people dancing. In this picture they are dancing slowly. They take up little space.

In the next picture people are dancing quickly. They take up much more space. People do not get bigger when they dance more quickly. They just take up more space.

a What happens to the space people use when they dance more quickly?

The same thing is true of particles. When they vibrate more quickly, they do not get bigger. But they do take up more space.

b Why does a metal expand when it is heated?

When a metal cools down, the particles vibrate more slowly. They take up less space. So the metal gets smaller. It **contracts**.

c What do we call it when a metal gets smaller?

Do all solids behave in the same way?

All solids expand when you heat them. But some expand more than others. This can cause lots of problems.

When engineers build a bridge, they have to remember that when it gets hot it will expand. They have to build special gaps for the bridge to expand into.

Look at the picture. It looks like two combs joined together. There are gaps between the teeth. This is called an expansion gap. You might see one on a road leading to a bridge. When the bridge gets hot it expands and the gap between the teeth gets smaller. This stops the bridge being damaged.

Do liquids and gases expand?

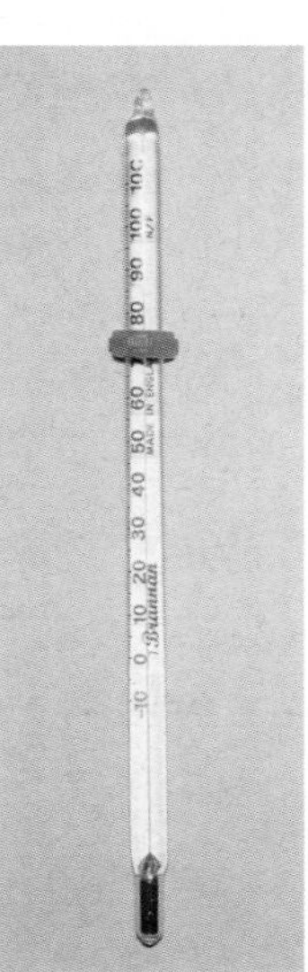

Liquids and gases also expand when heated. In fact they expand much more than solids. Look at the picture of the thermometer.

It works because the liquid inside the thermometer expands when it gets hot. The liquid contracts when it cools down. If the liquid did not expand when it got hot, the thermometer would not work.

KEY POINTS

- Materials expand when heated and contract when cooled.
- Materials expand because as the particles get more heat energy, they vibrate more quickly and take up more space.

QUESTIONS

Copy these sentences, choosing the correct words:

Materials expand when **heated/cooled** and contract when **heated/cooled**. This is because the particles take up **more/less** space as they vibrate more quickly.

16 CONVECTION

Why does hot air rise?

Corks float on water. This is because the corks are less dense than the water. Things that are less dense than water float. Things that are more dense than water sink.

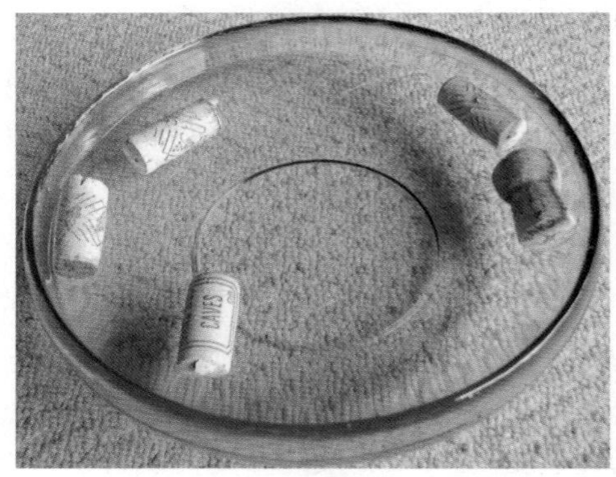

a What happens to things that are more dense than water?

Think of the atmosphere as being an ocean of air instead of an ocean of water. Just like water, some things float in the air and some things sink.

A helium balloon is less dense than air. It floats.

An apple is more dense than air. It sinks.

b Why does a helium balloon float?

Look at the picture of the hot air balloon. When the burner heats the air inside the balloon, the air particles vibrate more quickly. The air expands. This makes the air inside the balloon less dense than the surrounding air. It rises. This is called **convection.**

As the hot air is trapped in the balloon, the hot air takes the balloon up with it.

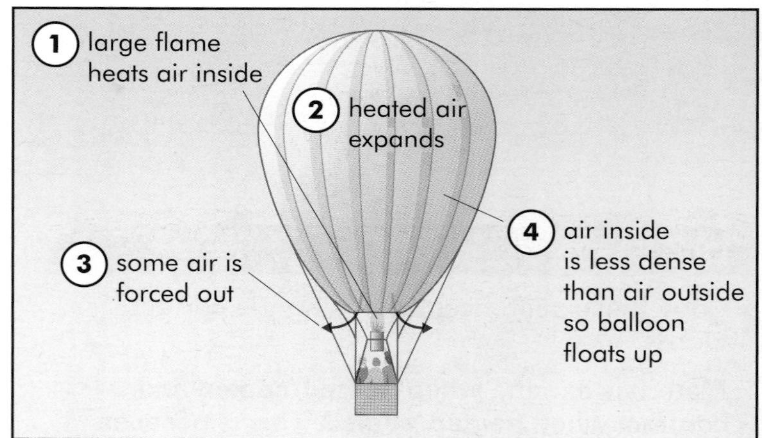
1 large flame heats air inside
2 heated air expands
3 some air is forced out
4 air inside is less dense than air outside so balloon floats up

c What do we call it when hot air rises?

When the air cools down, the opposite happens. It becomes more dense and falls. Hot air rises and cold air falls. This forms **convection currents**.

warmed water rises, carrying the purple colour with it
coloured crystal

Convection currents in liquids

Convection currents happen in liquids, just as they do in air. Look at the picture. It shows a beaker of water with a crystal of a dye in it.

The dye shows the hot water rising in the beaker. The dye rises because of convection currents.

d Why does the dye rise in the beaker?

Where else do we find convection currents?

Convection currents are happening all around us. The Sun warms the land. The land warms the air above it. The air rises. More air rushes in to take its place. This is wind.

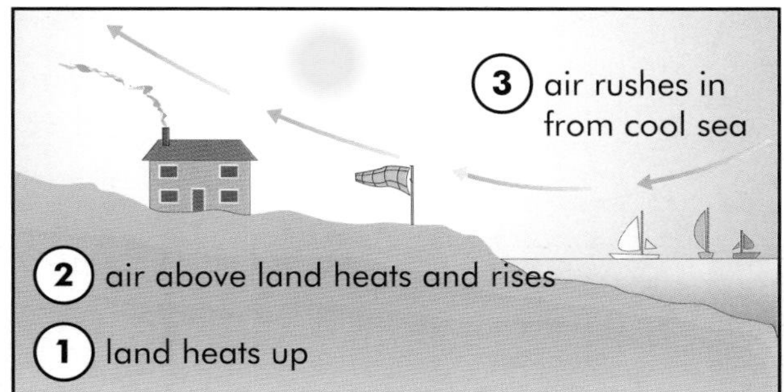
3 air rushes in from cool sea
2 air above land heats and rises
1 land heats up

QUESTIONS

Copy these sentences and fill in the spaces using the words below:

convection falls liquids rises

Hot air ________ and cold air ________ . These movements are called ________ currents. Convection currents also happen in ________ .

KEY POINTS

- Hot air rises. Cold air falls. It makes a convection current.

17 RADIATION AND ENERGY ESCAPE

How do we feel heat from the Sun?

We get heat energy on Earth from the Sun. The space between the Earth and the Sun is empty. There are no particles to move or vibrate. We call this empty space a **vacuum**.

a What do we call an empty space?

Conduction and convection both need particles to transfer heat. This means that heat energy cannot get to us from the Sun by conduction or convection.

We can get a clue about how the heat gets to us by standing in the sunshine. We can feel the heat from the Sun. If we put something between us and the Sun, by moving into the shade under a tree, we feel cooler. A tree can cast a heat shadow just like a light shadow. Heat must be like light.

Radiation

Heat reaches us from the Sun by **radiation**. Heat energy and light energy are very similar.

- They both travel in straight lines.
- They both travel at the same speed.
- They both travel through a vacuum.

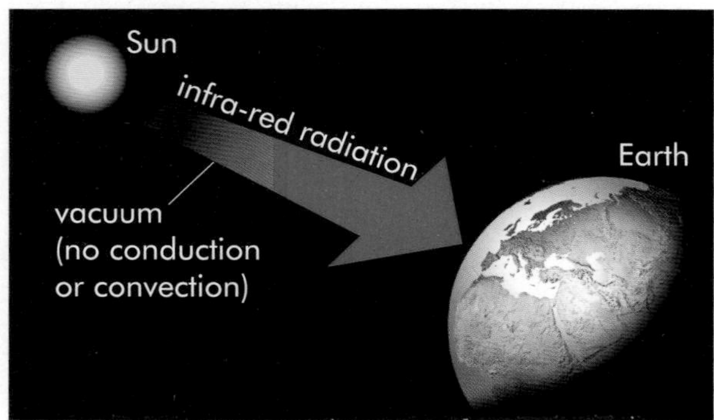

b How does heat reach us from the Sun?

c How are heat and light from the Sun similar?

There are some differences between heat energy and light energy.

- We can see light energy but we cannot see heat energy.
- Light energy can pass through glass easily, but heat energy cannot.

d How are heat and light different?

To see the heat energy from our bodies, we need a special camera. Look at the picture. You can see the left half of the man using a normal camera with light. You can see the right half using a special heat camera.

How can heat escape from your home?

Heat can be lost from your home by:

- conduction through the floor
- convection into the air
- radiation into the air.

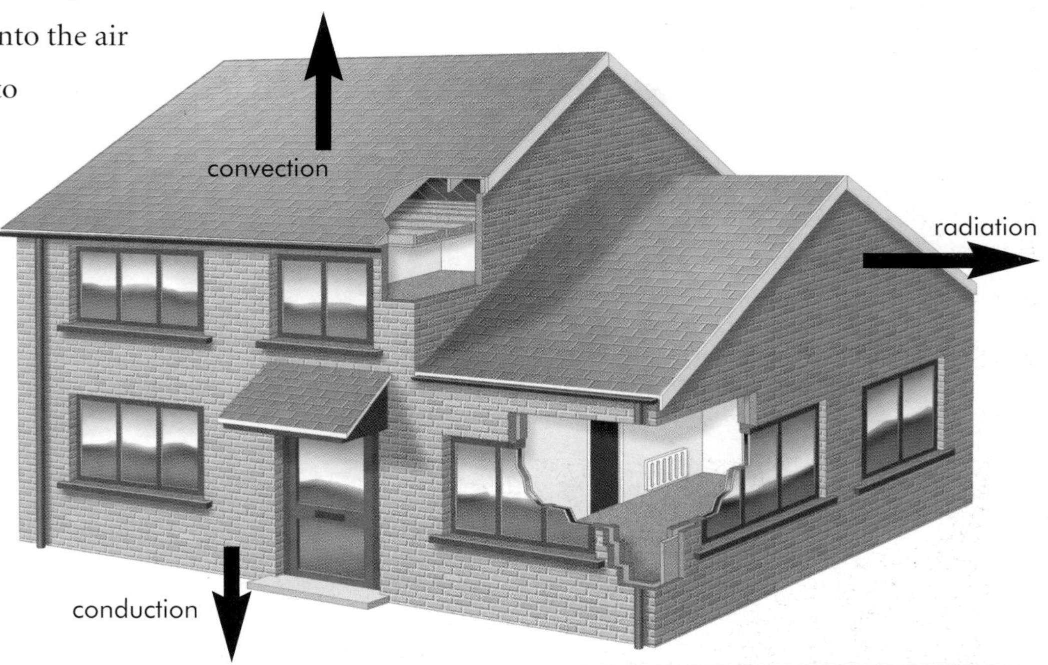

KEY POINTS

- Heat energy can travel in straight lines through a vacuum, by radiation.
- Objects can lose heat by conduction, convection and radiation.

QUESTIONS

Draw a picture of your home. Put three labels on it to show how it loses heat by conduction, convection and radiation.

18 EXPLAINING CHANGES OF STATE

What are changes of state?

Matter can exist in three different **states of matter**:

- solid
- liquid
- gas.

Look at the picture. It shows water in three different states – ice, water and steam.

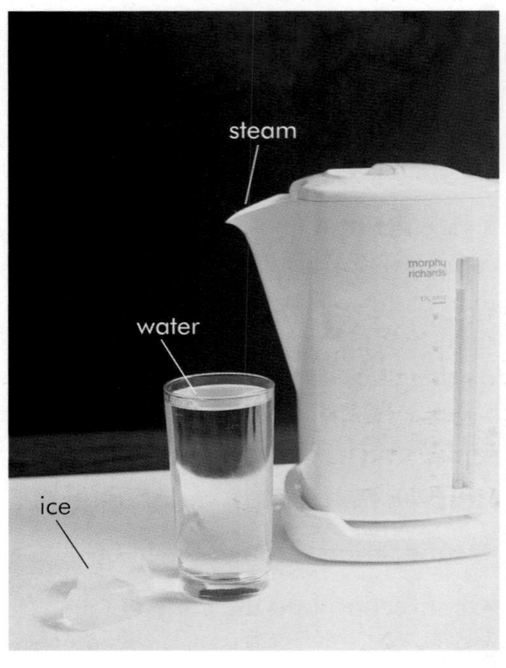

a What are the three states of matter?

Water can change its state from a solid, to a liquid, to a gas. This is called a **change of state**.

Water is a solid below 0 °C and a gas above 100 °C. It changes state at its **melting point** of 0 °C. It changes again at its **boiling point** of 100 °C. You need to put in or remove heat energy to make changes of state happen.

b At what temperature does water change its state from a liquid to a gas?

How does water change its state?

Look at the model of tennis balls held together by springs. The model represents the particles in a solid. When you heat the solid, the particles vibrate faster, just like the tennis balls.

Imagine that you heated the tennis balls and they vibrated so hard you broke some of the springs. The tennis balls are now free to move around anywhere they like. This is what happens when a solid melts into a liquid.

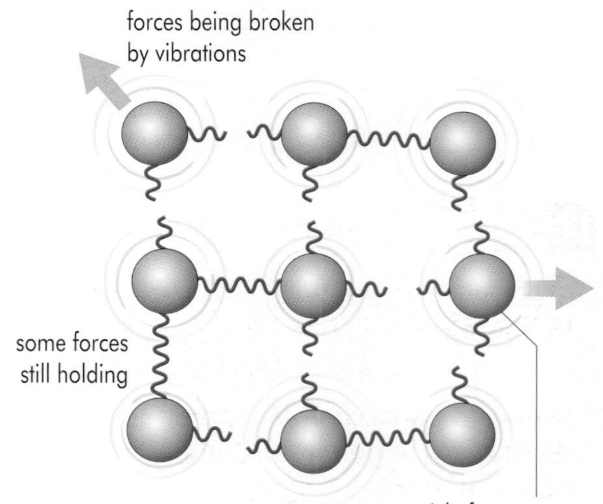

If you carried on heating the liquid, the particles would vibrate so fast that some of them would leave the liquid. This happens when a liquid is boiling. It is changing its state from a liquid to a gas.

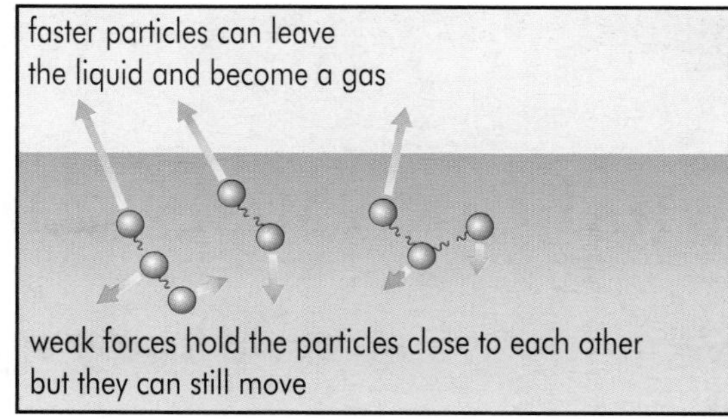
faster particles can leave the liquid and become a gas
weak forces hold the particles close to each other but they can still move

c What happens to some of the particles in a liquid when it boils?

What happens when you cool water that is a gas?

As the gas gets colder the particles vibrate more slowly. Eventually the gas condenses and turns back into liquid water. If you cool the water to 0 °C the particles will join together and form solid ice.

Why do you feel cold when you are wet?

When you are wet, you feel colder. This is because the water molecules get heat energy from your skin.

Some of the water molecules get enough heat energy to vibrate fast enough to **evaporate**. This makes your skin feel much colder. When water evaporates from your skin you lose heat energy. You feel cold.

d What do you feel when water evaporates from your skin?

QUESTIONS

Copy these sentences and fill in the spaces using the words below:

gas liquid solid

When water is below 0 °C it is a ________ . Between 0 °C and 100 °C it is a ________ . Above 100 °C water is a ________ .

KEY POINTS

- The three states of matter are solid, liquid and gas.
- A change of state happens when the particles gain or lose energy. They vibrate more or less.

J Magnets and electromagnets

J1 WHAT CAN A MAGNET DO?

What do we already know about magnets?

Magnets are rather strange. They pull some metals towards them. Sometimes they push metals away from them. They have no effect on other metals. It is hard to predict which metals will be affected by magnets.

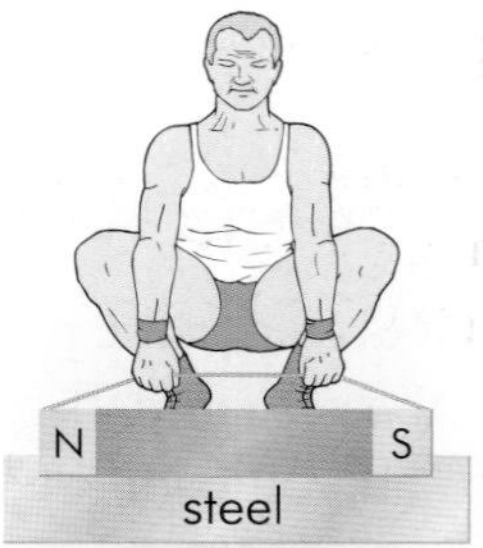

Magnets attract some metals...

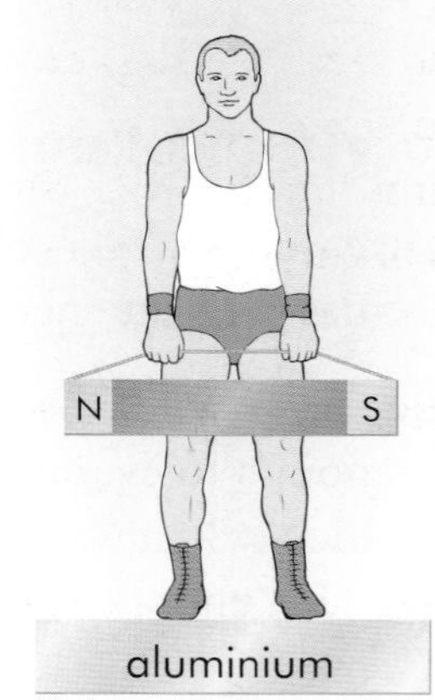

...but not others.

What is a magnet?

A magnet is often made of iron. It will pull or **attract** iron objects towards it. Steel is made mostly of iron. So a magnet will also pull steel towards it. There are only two other metals that are **magnetic**. They are called **nickel** and **cobalt**.

a Name three metals that are magnetic.

The most common magnets are long bars called **bar magnets**. The magnetic force is strongest at the ends. One end is called the **north pole**. The other end is called the **south pole**.

b What are the two ends of a bar magnet called?

A bar magnet

How do magnets affect each other?

Sometimes magnets pull towards each other. They **attract** each other. Sometimes magnets push each other away. They **repel** each other.

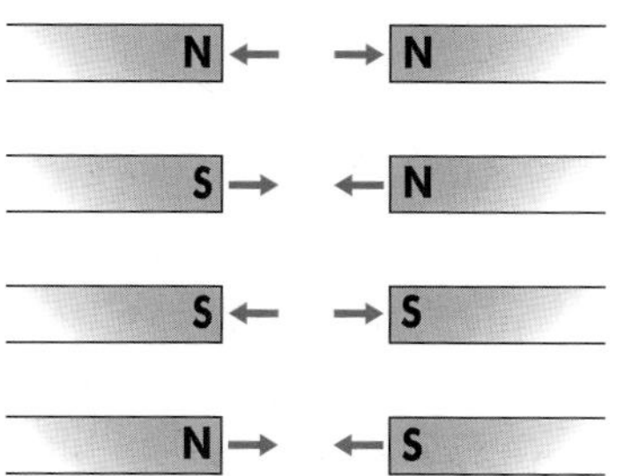
N
N
S
N
S
S
N
S

Look at the picture. It shows what happens when you put different poles close to each other.

- Like poles repel each other.
- Unlike poles attract each other.

c What would happen if you put the north pole of one magnet near to the south pole of another magnet?

How to make your own magnet

The easiest materials to make a magnet from are iron and steel. Needles are made from steel. Take a needle and stroke a strong magnet along it several times in the same direction. The needle will become a magnet.

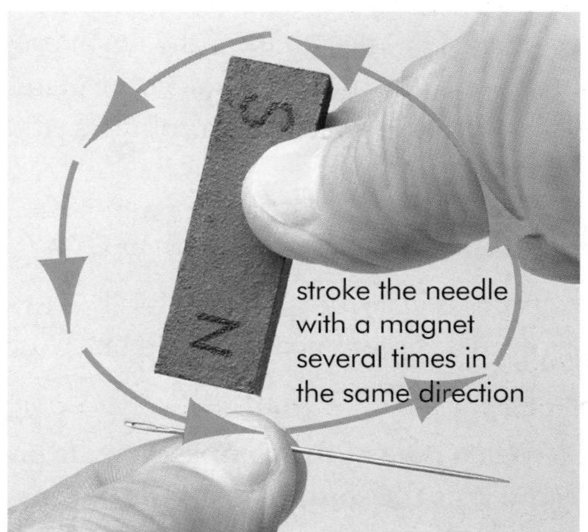
S
N
stroke the needle with a magnet several times in the same direction

d How can you make your own magnet?

When are magnets useful?

- Fridge magnets hold messages on to doors.
- Travel games, such as noughts and crosses, use magnets to stop the pieces slipping.
- Magnets are a good way of picking up pins.
- Magnets keep cupboard doors closed.

QUESTIONS

Copy these sentences and fill in the spaces using the words below:

attract iron repel

Magnetic materials are ________, steel, nickel and cobalt. Like poles ________ each other and unlike poles ________ each other.

KEY POINTS

- Magnetic materials are iron, steel, nickel and cobalt.
- Like poles repel and unlike poles attract.

J2 MAGNETIC FIELDS AND COMPASSES

What is a magnetic field?

Magnets are strongest at their poles. In fact the force of a magnet spreads out into the space around it. This is called the **magnetic field**. Magnetic fields are invisible. But we can show their shape using a sheet of paper and some iron filings. Look at the picture opposite.

1. Put the paper on top of the magnet.
2. Sprinkle iron filings on the sheet of paper.
3. The iron filings move and show the magnetic field.

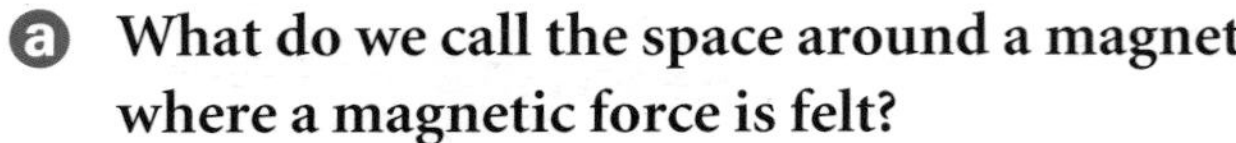

a What do we call the space around a magnet where a magnetic force is felt?

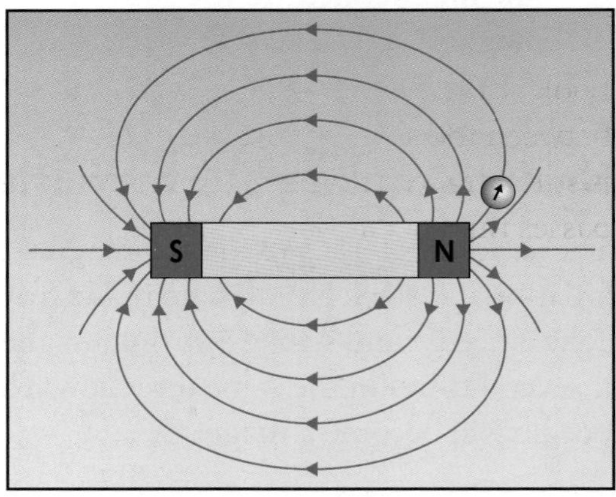

We can show the magnetic field more clearly by drawing **magnetic field lines**. The field lines never cross or touch each other. They just go from the north pole to the south pole of the magnet. Look at the picture opposite. The arrows show which way a compass would point.

How does a compass work?

A compass is just a tiny magnet. It is free to spin round. The compass points along the field lines. You can see this in the picture above of a bar magnet.

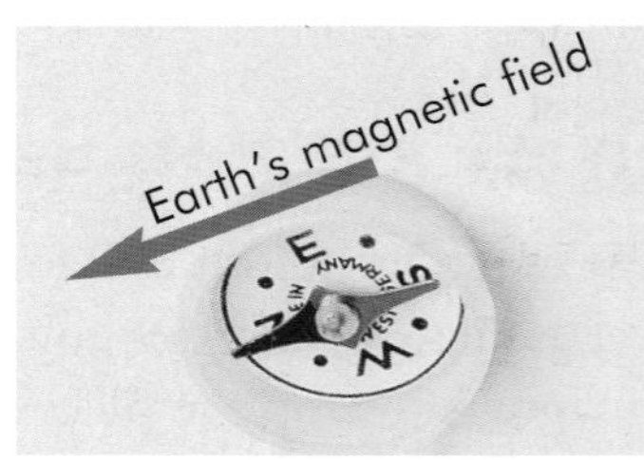

b Which pole of the compass needle points towards the south pole of the bar magnet?

Field lines between magnets

This is what the magnetic field lines look like when opposite poles come together.

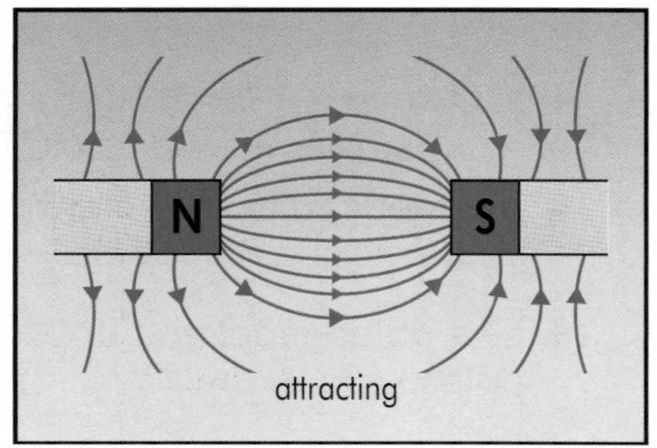

This is what the magnetic field lines look like when like poles come together.

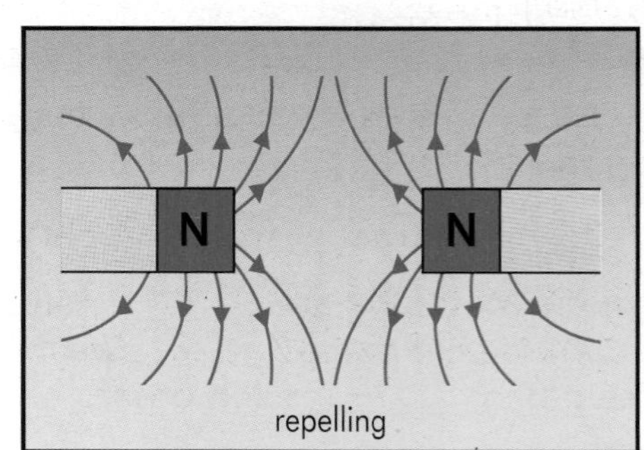

Can magnetic fields pass through other materials?

Look at the picture. It shows a magnet holding a paper clip up. The paper clip is attracted to the magnet. The paper clip is held by a piece of cotton thread. The magnetic field passes through paper.

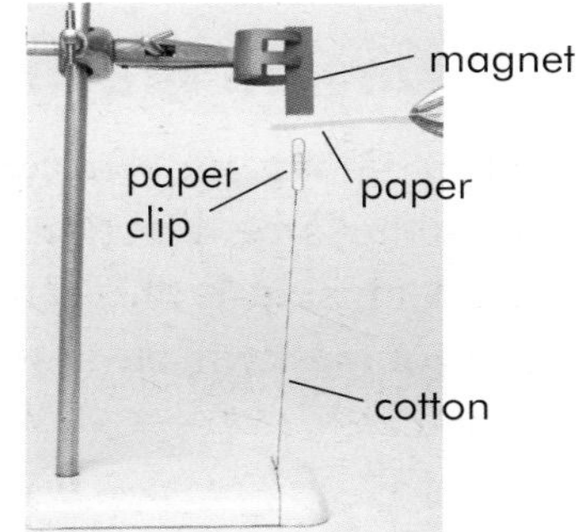

Look at the picture. It shows a sheet of aluminium between the magnet and the paper clip. The paper clip is still attracted to the magnet. The magnetic field passes through aluminium.

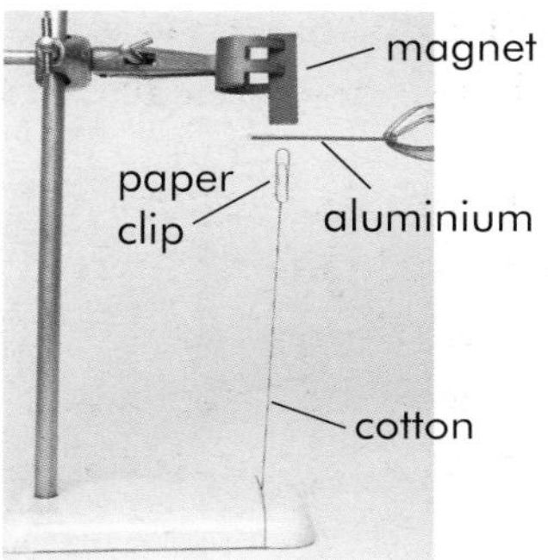

Look at the picture. It shows a sheet of steel between the magnet and the paper clip. The paper clip is not attracted to the magnet. The magnetic field cannot pass through the steel.

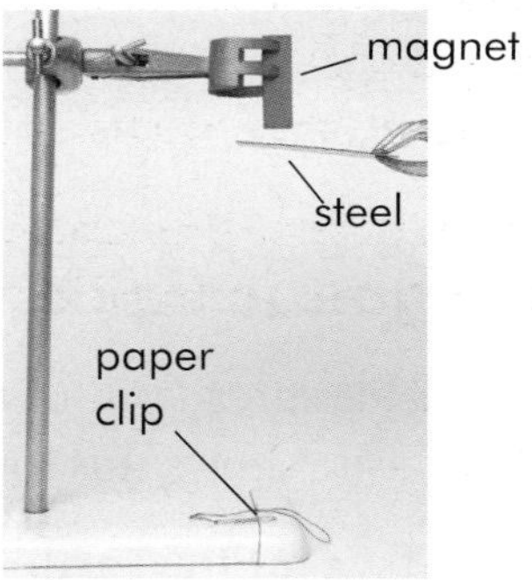

C Can a magnetic field pass through steel?

QUESTIONS

Copy these sentences and fill in the spaces using the words below:

aluminium field steel

Magnets produce a magnetic _______ . The field can pass through _______ but not through _______ .

KEY POINTS

- Magnets produce a magnetic field.
- The magnetic field cannot pass through steel.

J3 THE EARTH'S MAGNETIC FIELD

Which way do magnets point on the Earth?

If you let a compass turn freely, it will always end up pointing in the same direction. Imagine that the Earth has a magnet inside. It causes the **Earth's magnetic field**. The compass will always point towards the North Pole of the Earth.

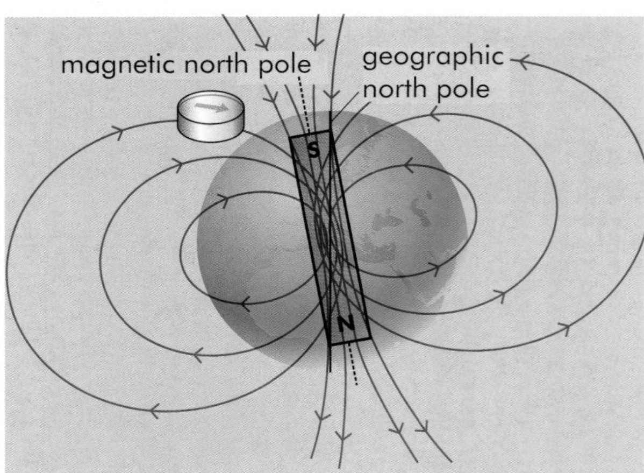

a **Which metal inside the Earth could produce the magnetic field?**

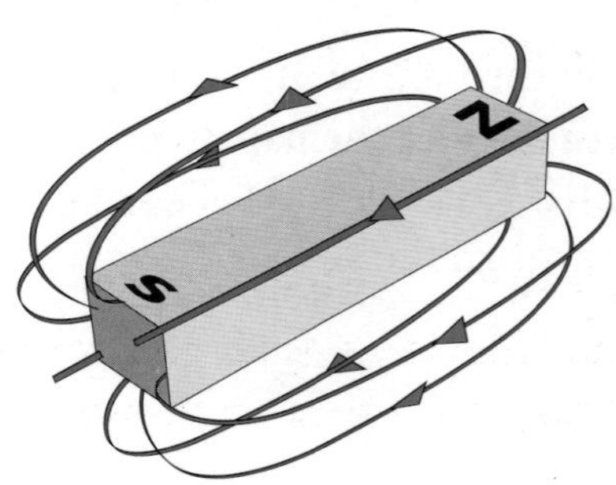

Are magnetic fields flat?

Magnetic fields spread out in all directions. The picture opposite shows this for a bar magnet.

This is also true for the Earth. If you took a compass to the North Pole it would try to point straight downwards. This is not much use for finding your direction.

b **Why would a compass not be much use at the North Pole?**

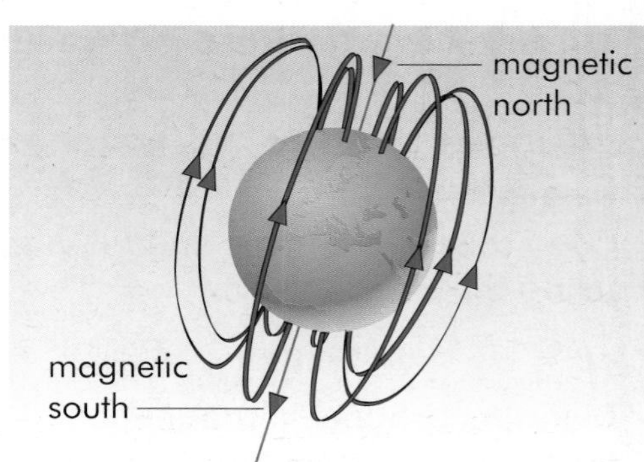

Using the Earth's magnetic field

People have known about the Earth's magnetic field for about 1000 years. Lodestone is a rock found in the ground. It contains iron and is magnetic. The picture shows lodestone.

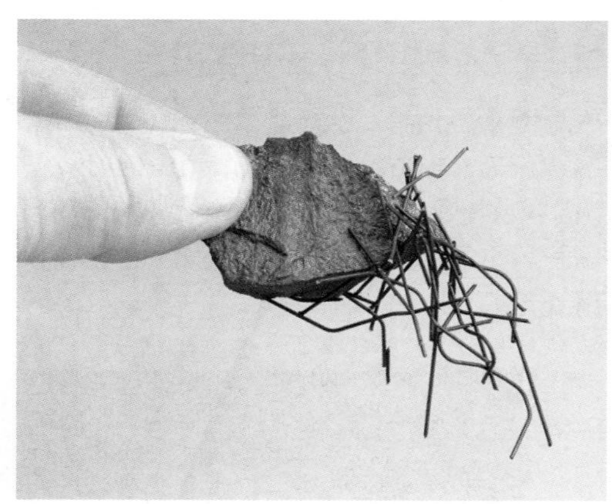

People used to think lodestone had magical powers. They made compasses out of it so they could find their way across the sea in boats. People also used the position of the Sun and stars to find their way.

Today ships and aircraft all use compasses to tell them which direction they are travelling in. A compass will work when it is cloudy, dark or even in thick fog.

c Why is navigation using a compass better than using the Sun or stars?

When compasses don't work

You saw from the paper clip experiment that magnetic fields do not pass through steel. If you put a piece of steel near a compass, the compass needle will move and point to the steel.

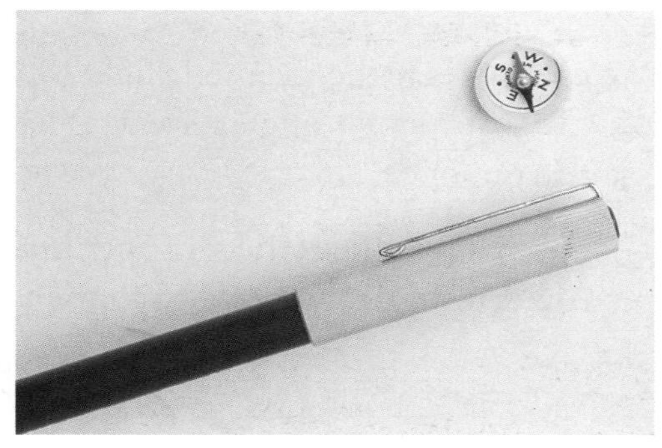

Look at the picture. It shows the compass needle pointing to a steel pen instead of the North Pole.

Some areas of Scotland have a lot of iron in the ground. This stops compasses working properly. The compass tries to point to the iron in the ground.

d Why should we be careful when using a compass in some areas of Scotland?

QUESTIONS

Copy these sentences and fill in the spaces using the words below:

iron   points

A compass ________ towards the North Pole of the Earth. It will not work close to ________ or steel.

KEY POINTS

- A compass points towards the North Pole of the Earth's magnetic field.
- A compass will not work if it is close to iron or steel.

J4 HOW CAN ELECTRICITY MAKE A MAGNET?

Does electric current have a magnetic effect?

When we pass electric current through a wire, it makes a magnetic field around the wire. Look at the picture. An electric current is passing through the wire. The iron filings have moved to show the magnetic field.

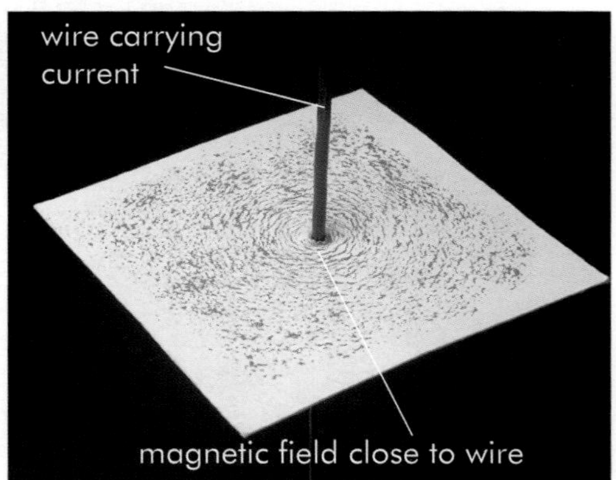

a What happens when we pass an electric current through a wire?

We can increase the magnetic field by using a coil of wire instead of a single wire. Look at the picture opposite.

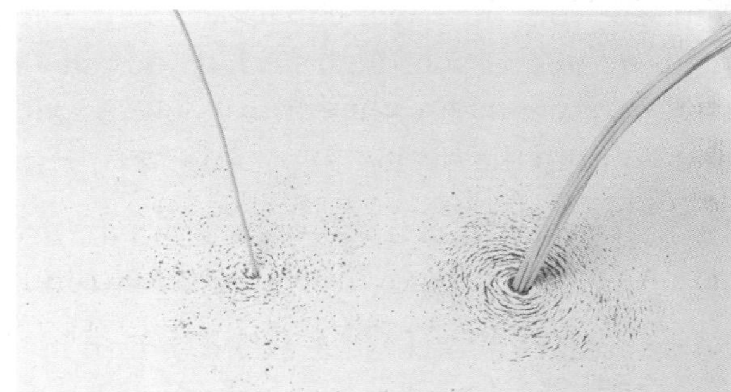

b Which produces the stronger magnetic field, a single wire or a coil of wire?

What is an electromagnet?

If we wrap the wire round some magnetic metal, it makes a much stronger magnetic field. This is called an **electromagnet**.

Look at picture A. It shows the wire coiled round an iron nail. The electromagnet is strong enough to pick up a paper clip.

c What do we call it when a coil of wire carrying an electric current is wrapped round an iron nail?

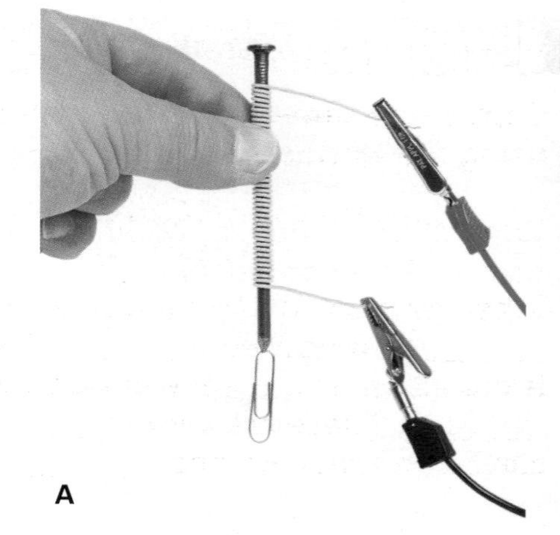

A

We can make the magnet stronger by passing a bigger current through the wire. Look at picture B. With more current the nail can pick up two paper clips.

We can make it even stronger by putting more coils around the nail. Look at picture C. With more coils it can attract three paper clips.

d **Describe two ways that we can make an electromagnet stronger.**

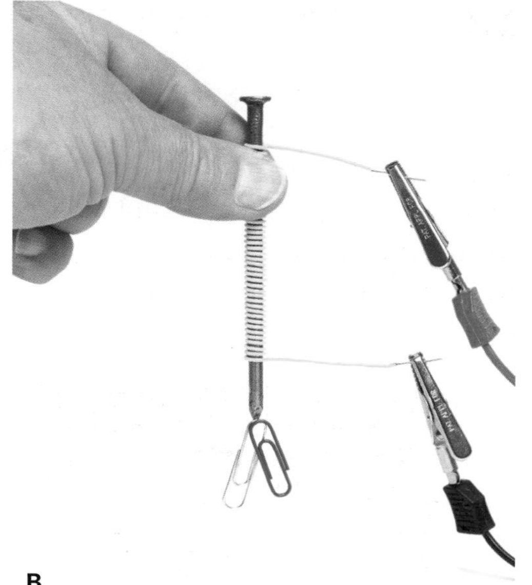

B

What are electromagnets used for?

Electromagnets are useful because:

- they can make very strong magnets
- we can switch them on and off by turning the current off.

People use electromagnets for sorting magnetic metals like iron and steel from other materials. This makes it easier to recycle iron and steel.

e **Why do people use an electromagnet rather than a bar magnet to sort out iron and steel from other scrap?**

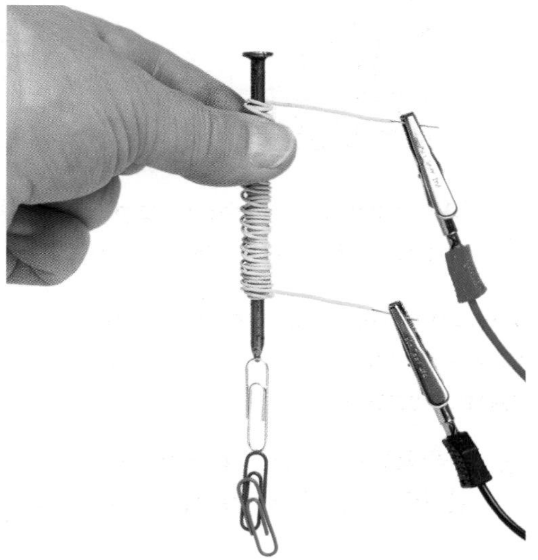

C

QUESTIONS

Copy these sentences and fill in the spaces using the words below:

electromagnet magnetic off strong wire

When an electric current passes through a ________ it produces a ________ field. If the wire is coiled round a magnetic metal we have an ________ . These are very ________ magnets and can be switched on and ________ .

KEY POINTS

- If we pass an electric current through a wire, it produces a magnetic field.
- If we coil the wire round a magnetic metal, it makes an electromagnet.

K Light

K1 HOW DOES LIGHT TRAVEL?

Where does light come from?

Light is a form of energy. Things that are very hot have lots of energy. Very hot things give off light as well as heat energy.

Something that gives off light is called a **source** of light. The Sun is very hot. It is a source of light.

a **Why does the Sun give off light?**

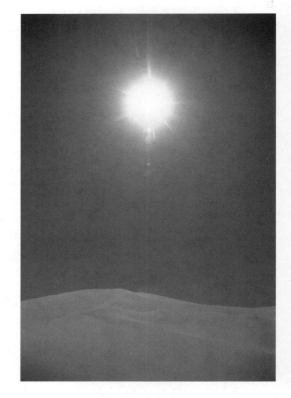

Empty space, where there is no air or anything else, is called a **vacuum**. Light energy can travel through empty space. It does not need a material or **medium** to travel through. Like heat energy, light energy travels best through a vacuum. It can also travel through glass, air and water.

b **Apart from a vacuum, what else can light travel through?**

How fast does light travel?

Light is fast. It travels about 300 000 000 metres in one second. This is hard to imagine. It means that light would get from England to America in one-hundredth of a second.

The Sun is much further away than America. It takes light about 8 minutes to get to us from the Sun. The light from the next nearest star takes about 4 years to get to us.

c **How long does it take light to get to us from the Sun?**

Does light travel in straight lines or curves?

Light travels in straight lines. This is why **shadows** form. Because light travels in straight lines, the shadow has a sharp edge.

Look at the picture. You can see that the shadow is the same shape as the hand. This is because light travels in straight lines.

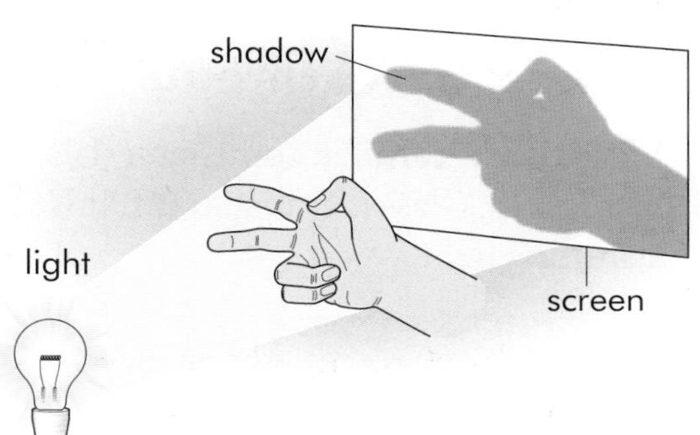

d What sort of lines does light travel in?

How can we show that light travels in straight lines?

Look at the picture. It shows three pieces of card with holes in them. If the holes are not lined up in a straight line, the light does not get through all the holes.

Look at this picture. When the holes are all in a straight line, the light can get through to the screen.

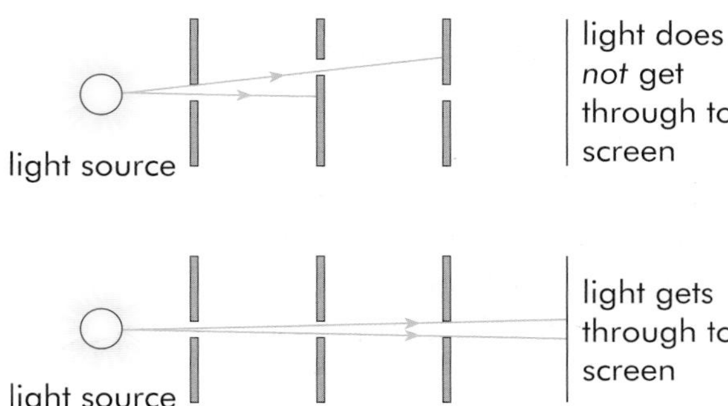

The arrows on the pictures show which way the light is travelling. We call pictures like this **ray diagrams**.

e What do we call pictures that show light as lines with arrows showing the direction of the light?

QUESTIONS

Copy these sentences and fill in the spaces using the words below:

light ray straight

Very hot object give out ________ . Light travels in ________ lines. If we draw these straight lines and put arrows on them we have drawn a ________ diagram.

KEY POINTS

- Very hot objects give out light. They are sources of light.
- Light travels in straight lines.

K2 MATERIALS AND LIGHT

Can light travel through materials?

Light can travel through some materials. We call this **transmission**. Glass is **transparent**. It is very good at transmitting light.

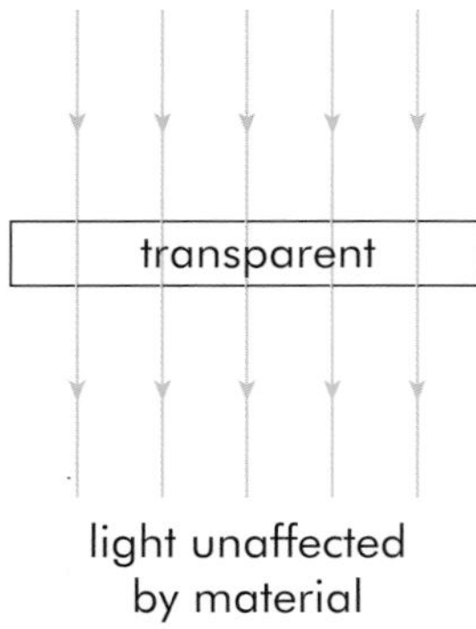

ⓐ **What do we call materials that are good at transmitting light?**

Some materials let light through, but are not quite so good at transmitting light. They **scatter** the light as it passes through. These materials are called **translucent**.

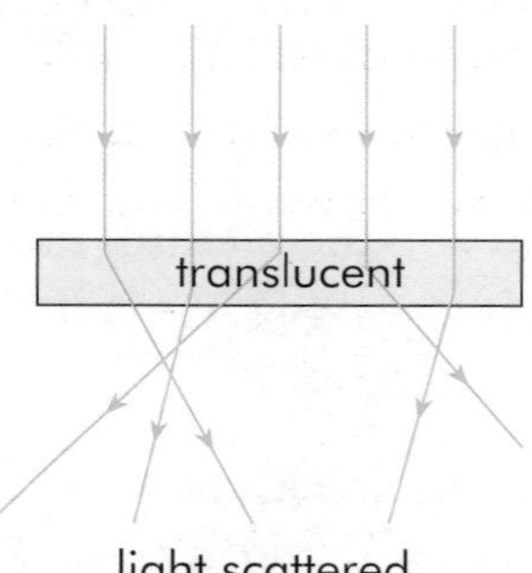

Some windows made of glass or plastic are translucent. They let daylight into a house, but stop people outside seeing clearly inside the house.

ⓑ **What do we call materials that scatter light as it passes through?**

Some materials do not let light pass through at all. Some light is reflected. Some is absorbed. These materials are called **opaque**.

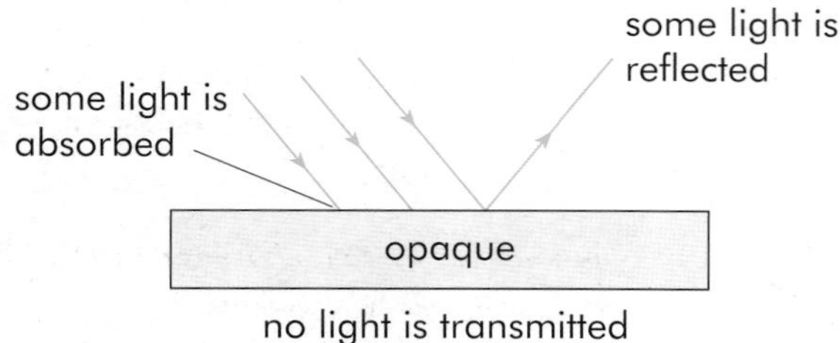

ⓒ **What do we call materials that do not let light pass through?**

What happens when light hits an opaque material?

If the opaque surface is very smooth, like a mirror, the light is reflected in an organised way.

If the surface is rough, like a sheet of paper, the light is scattered as it is reflected.

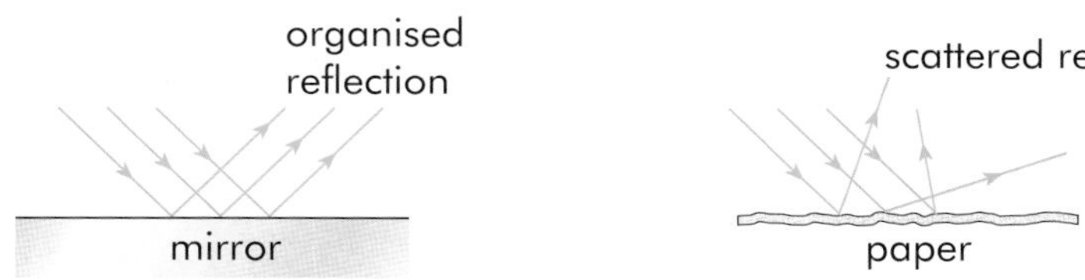

Light reflected in an organised way makes a **reflection**. This is why you can see your reflection in a mirror.

But you cannot see your reflection in a sheet of paper. The light is scattered in all directions.

d **Why can't you see your reflection in a sheet of paper?**

QUESTIONS

Copy these sentences and fill in the spaces using the words below:

absorb   opaque   passes   translucent

Light ________ through transparent materials. ________ materials let light through but scatter the light. ________ materials do not let light through. Opaque materials reflect light and ________ light.

KEY POINTS

- Light passes through transparent materials.
- Light passes through translucent materials but gets scattered.
- Light does not pass through opaque materials.
- Opaque materials reflect and absorb light.

K3 HOW DO WE SEE THINGS?

How do we see things?

If you look at a candle flame you can see the light that it is giving out. The light travels in straight lines. Some of the light enters your eye and you can see the flame.

The candle flame is a source of light. Sources of light are called **luminous**. Things that are not sources of light are called **non-luminous**.

a What do we call things that are not sources of light?

How can we see non-luminous things?

A non-luminous object such as a book is not a source of light. You can see the book because it reflects light. This light comes from a luminous object like the candle flame. If the candle flame went out, you could no longer see the book.

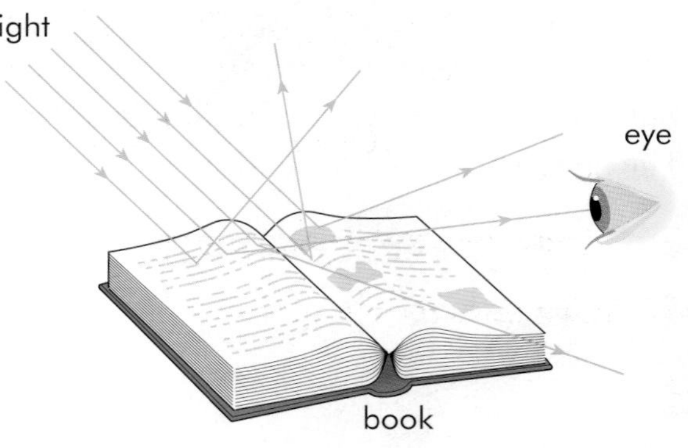

The Sun is a source of light. The Moon is not a source of light. We can only see the Moon because it reflects light from the Sun.

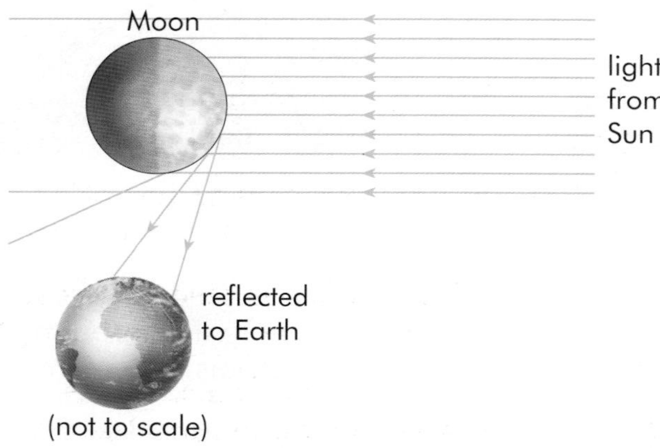

b Why can we see the Moon?

What does your eye do?

Light has to enter your eye for you to see anything. If no light enters your eye, it is dark and you cannot see. The eye is rather like a camera.

- The light enters the eye through a hole called the **pupil**. The pupil can get bigger or smaller to let in more or less light.
- The **lens** focuses the light so that you can see a sharp image.
- The light hits the back of the eye. This is called the **retina**. It is rather like the film in a camera.

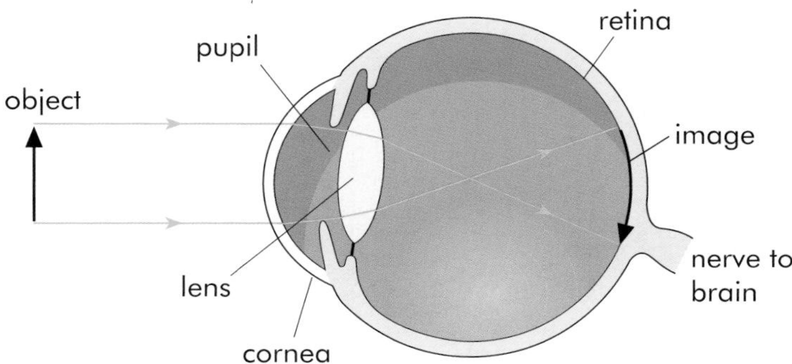

c **Where does light enter the eye?**

d **What does the lens do?**

QUESTIONS

Copy these sentences and fill in the spaces using the words below:

enters   luminous   reflect

_______ objects give off light. Non-luminous objects _______ light. You can only see an object when light from the object _______ your eye.

KEY POINTS

- Luminous objects give off light.
- Non-luminous objects reflect light.
- You can only see an object when light from the object enters your eye.

K4 HOW DOES LIGHT REFLECT?

What happens to reflected light?

Light travels in straight lines. When it hits a smooth flat shiny surface it is reflected. A mirror has a smooth flat shiny surface.

a What kind of surface does a mirror have?

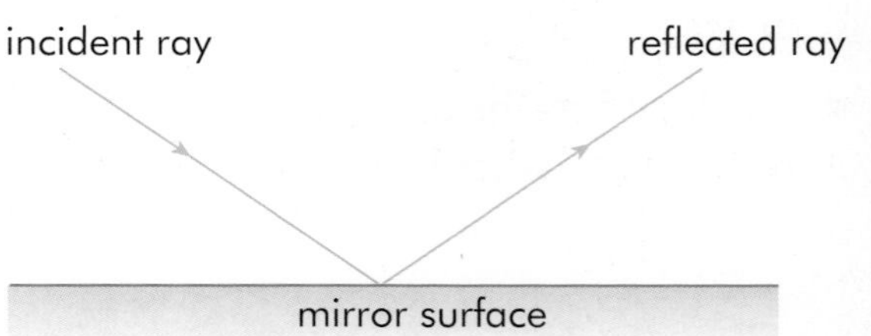

Look at the picture opposite. The ray of light that hits the surface is called the **incident ray**. The ray of light that is reflected is called the **reflected ray**.

Look at the picture below. If a ray of light hits a mirror at right angles, it is reflected back in exactly the same direction as it came from.

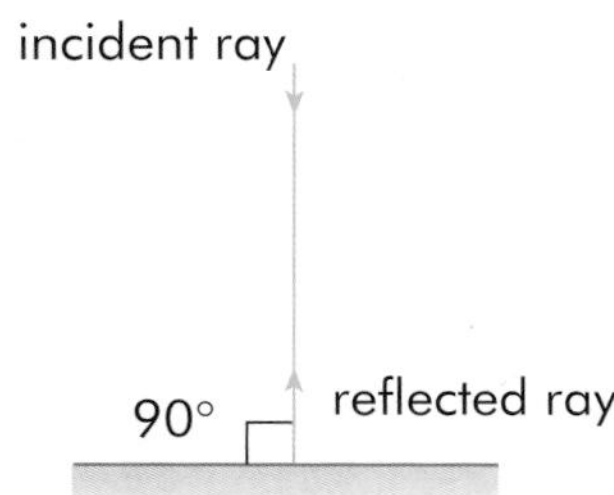

What happens with other angles?

Imagine a line at right angles to the mirror. We call this line the **normal**. The angle between the incident ray and the normal is always the same as the angle between the reflected ray and the normal.

This is hard to understand. So look at the pictures. Look at the angle between the incident ray and the normal. Now look at the angle between the reflected ray and the normal. The two angles are the same in each picture.

b What do we know about the angle between the incident ray and the normal and the angle between the reflected ray and the normal?

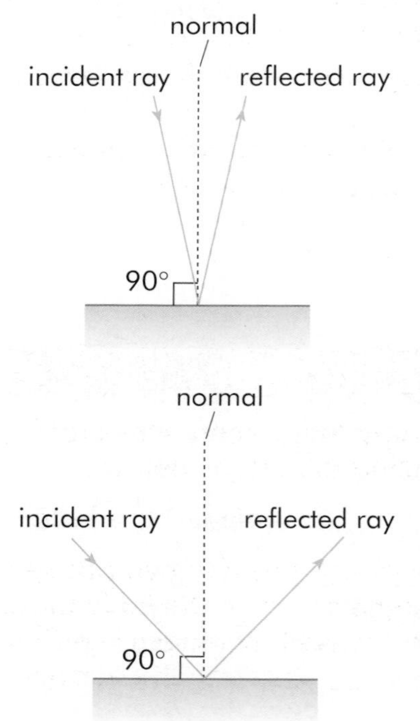

How are reflected images formed?

When you look in a mirror, you see a reflection. If you look at writing in a mirror, it is back to front. The boy is holding a piece of paper with an F written on it. When he looks in the mirror, the F is back to front.

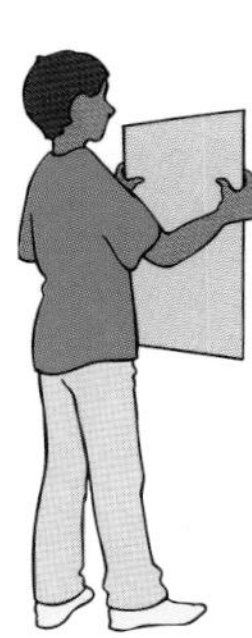

Have you ever wondered why the word 'AMBULANCE' is written back to front on an ambulance? So that when car drivers see the word in their mirrors, it will look the right way round.

c Why is the word 'AMBULANCE' written back to front on an ambulance?

The reflection in a mirror always looks back to front. But it never looks upside down. Scientists call a picture going back to front **lateral inversion**.

d What do we call it when things appear back to front in a mirror?

QUESTIONS

Copy these sentences and fill in the spaces using the words below:

normal   reflected   shiny

A mirror has a flat smooth ________ surface. The angle between the incident ray and the ________ is always the same as the angle between the ________ ray and the normal.

KEY POINTS

- Mirrors have flat smooth shiny surfaces. They make back-to-front pictures.
- The angle between the incident ray and the normal is always the same as the angle between the reflected ray and the normal.

K5 CAN LIGHT BE BENT?

What is refraction?

You know that light travels only in straight lines. When it is reflected, it still travels in straight lines, but in the opposite direction.

There is another way that light can be made to change direction.

Look at the picture of a pencil in a beaker of water. The pencil looks broken, but it is not really broken. When the light went from the water into the air, the light changed direction. We call this **refraction.**

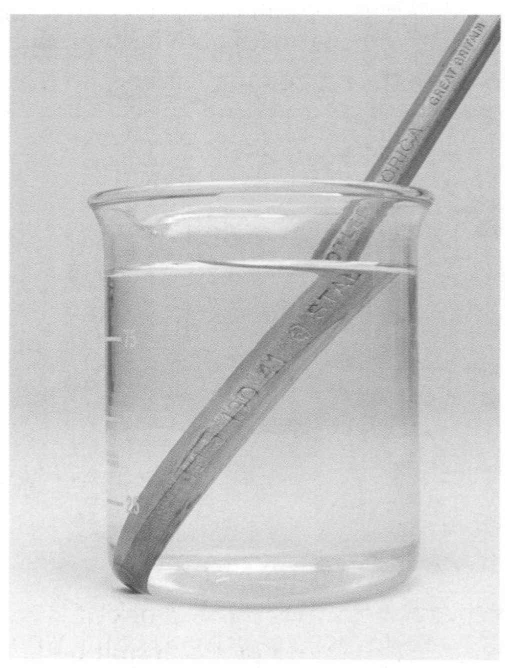

(a) What do we call it when light goes from one material to another and changes direction?

Light changes direction when it passes from one material to another. Look at the picture below. It shows a ray of light going into a glass block. The ray of light changes direction.

The ray of light goes through the glass and leaves the other side. It changes direction again as it leaves.

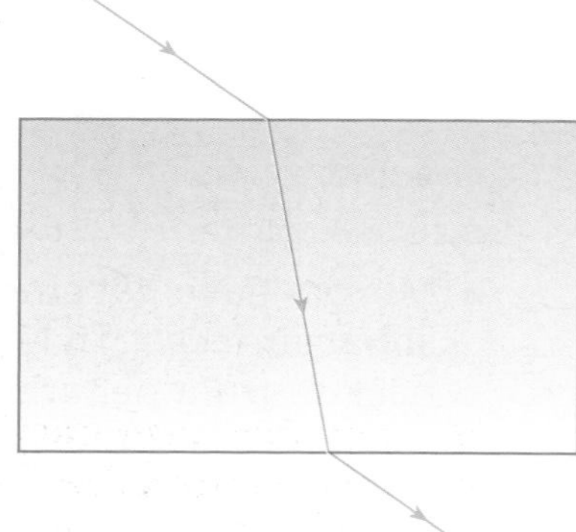

(b) How many times does the ray of light change direction when it goes through a block of glass?

Why is it difficult to catch fish in a pond?

The water in a pond always looks shallower than it really is. This is because the light changes direction when it leaves the water.

Look at the picture. The solid fish is where the fish really is. The dotted fish is where we think the fish is. Our eyes do not realise that the light has changed direction. This is why it is difficult to catch fish in a pond.

light is refracted at the water surface

where light appears to come from

The fish looks closer to the surface than it really is.

What is a spectrum?

White light contains lots of different colours. When they pass from glass into air, they all change direction by different amounts.

Look at the picture. The triangular block of glass is called a **prism**. We can use a prism to split up light into its different colours. These colours are called the **spectrum**. They are the colours of the rainbow.

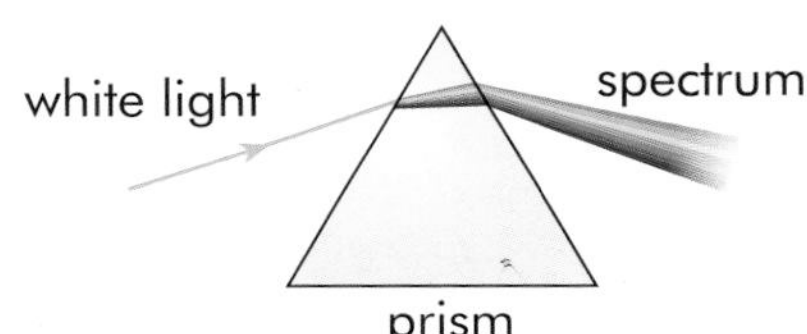

Raindrops act like tiny prisms. They split up sunlight into its different colours and make the rainbow.

C **What is a spectrum?**

QUESTIONS

Copy these sentences and fill in the spaces using the words below:

changes spectrum prism

Light ________ direction when it passes from one material to another. A ________ can split up light into a ________ .

KEY POINTS

- Light changes direction when it passes from one material to another.
- A prism can split up white light into a spectrum.

K6 HOW CAN WE CHANGE COLOUR?

How do filters change white light?

If we shine white light at a green filter, only the green light comes through. The green light has been transmitted. The filter absorbs all the other colours and stops them passing through.

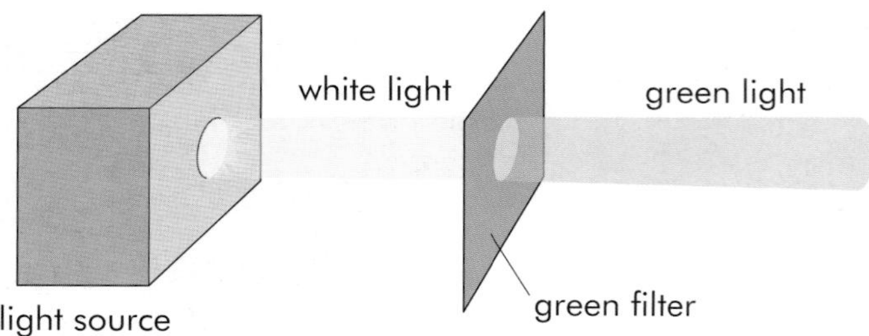

We can prove this by putting a red filter in the path of the green light. There is only green light meeting the red filter. A red filter will only let red light through. So nothing gets through.

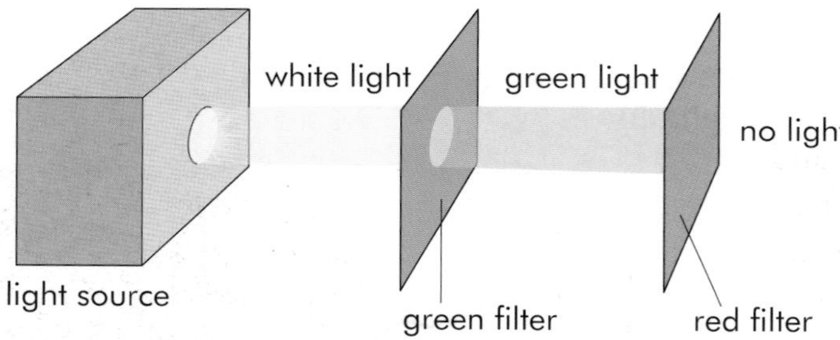

Each coloured filter lets only its own colour through. It absorbs all other colours.

a What colour of light will a blue filter let through?

Can we make new colours?

You are used to mixing paint in art lessons and making new colours. But light works differently.

Look at the picture. It shows three different coloured lights – red, green and blue. When the three colours are mixed together there are some surprising results.

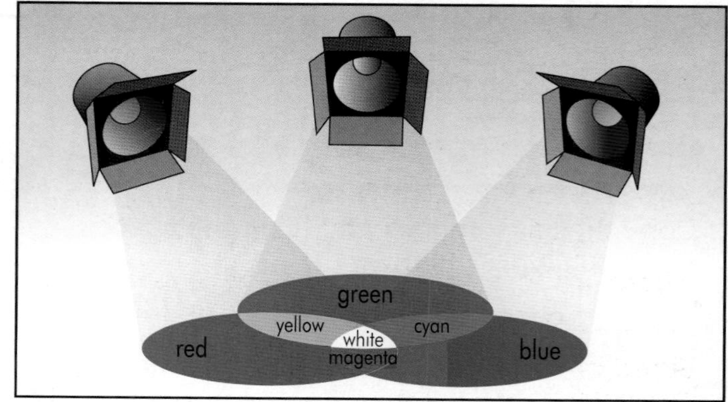

b What colour is made when red and green light are mixed together?

c What colour is made when red, green and blue light are mixed together?

Red, green and blue are called **primary colours**. We can use them to make any other colours we need.

d What do we call red, green and blue?

Why do things look coloured?

When you see a red ball, it looks red because it is reflecting red light. White light is falling on the ball. It absorbs all the colours except red. It reflects the red light into your eye. So you see the ball as red.

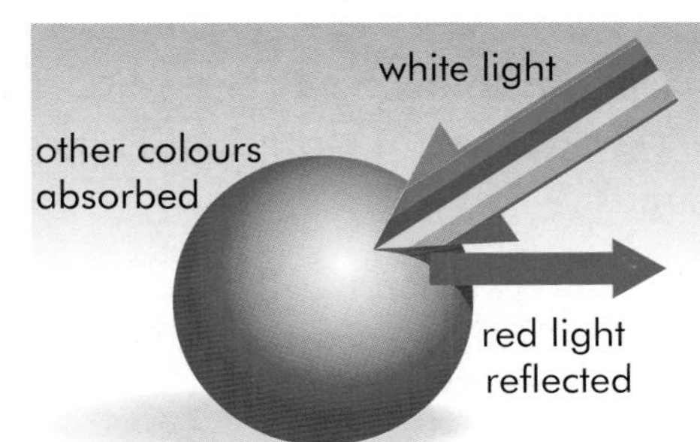

Look at the picture. It shows white light hitting the red ball. Remember that white light is a mixture of different colours. The ball is only reflecting the red part of the white light.

e Why does the ball look red?

How do colour televisions work?

A TV screen has thousand of red, green and blue dots on it. Each dot can give off different amounts of light. By altering this, we get all the different colours that we need.

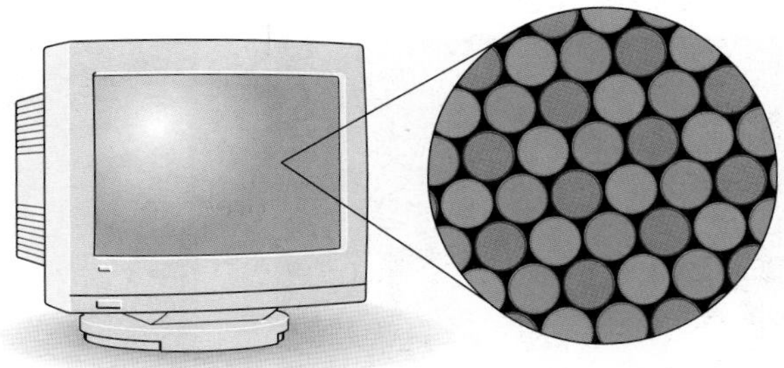

QUESTIONS

Copy these sentences and fill in the spaces using the words below:

green absorbs red spectrum blue

A blue filter lets only ________ light through. It ________ all other colours.

There are three primary colours. They are red, ________ and blue.

A red ball looks red because it reflects ________ light. We can mix the primary colours to make all the other colours of the ________ .

KEY POINTS

- A coloured filter lets only its own coloured light through. It absorbs all other colours.
- There are three primary colours – red, green and blue.
- By mixing primary colours together we can make all the other colours we need.

L Sound and hearing

L1 HOW ARE DIFFERENT SOUNDS MADE?

How are sounds made?

When something moves backwards and forwards quickly, we say it is **vibrating**. Things that vibrate make sounds.

A bee buzzes when it is flying. Its wings move backwards and forwards very fast, making the buzzing noise.

a Why does a bee buzz when it flies?

Musical instruments also have parts that vibrate.

The strings on a guitar vibrate when you pluck them.

The skin on a drum vibrates when you hit it.

The air inside a recorder vibrates when you blow down it.

b Say what vibrates when a guitar, drum and recorder make a sound.

How high or low?

The **pitch** of a note is how high or low the note is. The pitch depends on how fast something is vibrating. We measure the pitch by counting how many times the thing vibrates each second. This is called the **frequency**.

c How do we measure pitch?

Something vibrating very fast makes a high-pitched note. It has a high frequency. Something vibrating very slowly makes a low-pitched note. It has a low frequency.

There are three ways of making a guitar string vibrate more quickly:

- make the string shorter
- make the string tighter
- use a thinner string.

How loud or soft?

How loud or soft a sound is depends on the **amplitude** of the sound. Loud sounds have big vibrations or a big amplitude. Quiet sounds have small vibrations or a small amplitude.

d **If a sound has big vibrations, what does it sound like?**

Looking at sounds

We can see how sounds are different by drawing graphs of them. These first two pictures show a high sound and a low sound.

Amplitude →
Time →
high . . .

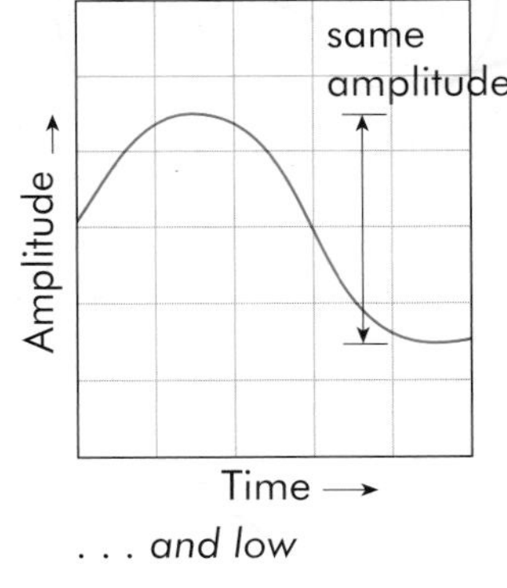

. . . and low

These two pictures show a quiet sound and a loud sound.

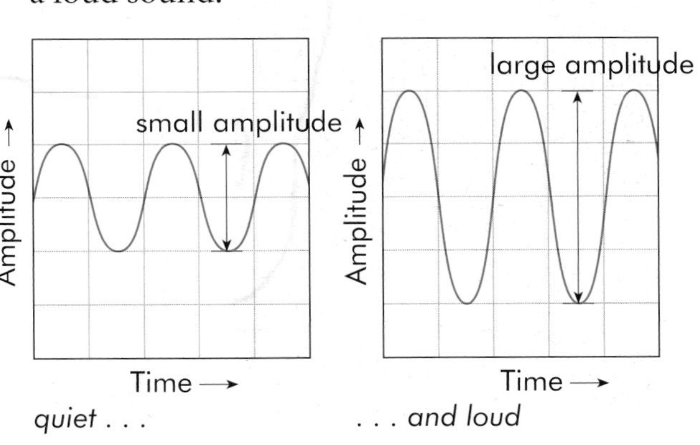

quiet . . .

. . . and loud

QUESTIONS

Copy these sentences and fill in the spaces using the words below:

loud quickly vibrates

Sound is made when something ________ . If it vibrates ________, it makes a high-pitched sound. ________ sounds are made by big vibrations.

KEY POINTS

- Sound is made when something vibrates
- High-pitched sounds happen when something vibrates very quickly.
- Loud sounds are made by big vibrations.

L2 HOW DOES SOUND TRAVEL THROUGH SOLIDS, LIQUIDS AND GASES?

Does sound need something to travel through?

Sound travels out from a vibrating object, through the air, to your ears. Sound needs a **medium** to travel through. Air is the medium. If there was no air, there would be no sound.

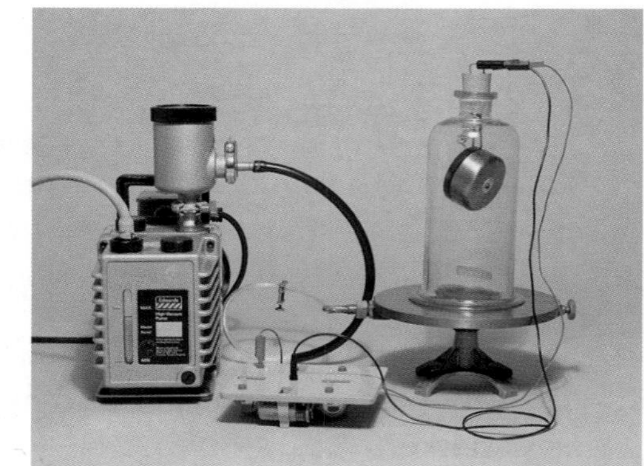

Look at the picture. It shows a bell inside a glass jar. A pump works to pump out all the air. When the glass jar contains air, we can hear the bell ring. As the air is pumped out, the bell gets quieter until we can no longer hear it ringing. This is because there is no air to vibrate.

a Why can't we hear the bell when there is no air in the jar?

How does sound travel through the air?

Sound travels through the air by making the gas particles vibrate. Eventually they reach our ears and we hear the sound.

b How does sound travel through the air?

The tuning fork makes areas where the air particles are closer together . . .

Sound moves away from the source.

vibrating tuning fork

. . . and areas where the air particles are further apart.

How does sound travel through water?

The particles in water are much closer together than the particles in air. They can pass on the vibrations more quickly than in air. This means that water is much better at carrying sound.

Whales can communicate with each other across the oceans. That would be impossible in air. Even the loudest person can only be heard about a mile away.

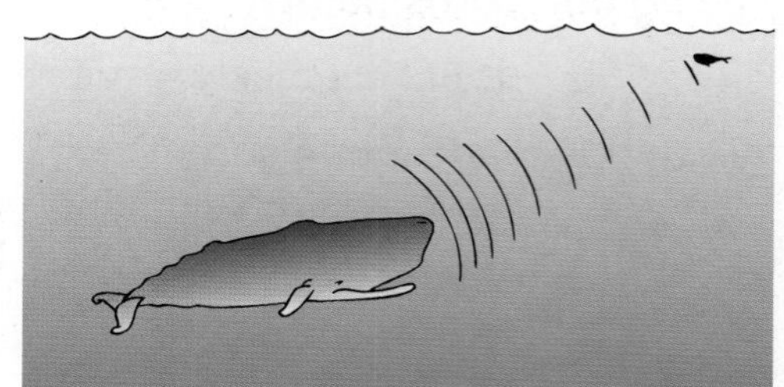

How does sound travel through a solid?

Sound travels through a solid even quicker than through water. This is because the particles in solids are much closer together and pass the vibrations on very quickly. The sound of a train coming can be heard through the rails, long before the sound reaches us through the air.

C Which carries sound the best, a solid, water, or air?

How can we measure the speed of sound?

Rachel and Joey stand 150 metres away from a high wall. Rachel bangs two blocks of wood together. Joey times how long it takes for the echo to come back. It takes about one second.

Joey calculates that the sound travelled 300 metres in one second.

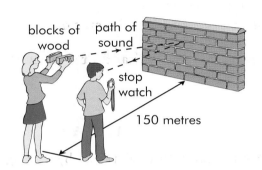

blocks of wood
path of sound
stop watch
150 metres

Which is faster, sound or light?

Light travels about a million times faster than sound. This is why we see the lightning flash before we hear the sound of thunder. The table shows some other differences between sound and light.

Sound	Light
travels slowly	travels fast
needs a medium to travel through	can travel through a vacuum
can go round corners	can't go round corners

QUESTIONS

Copy these sentences and fill in the spaces using the words below:

faster medium light solid

Sound needs a ________ to travel through. Sound travels fastest in a ________ . But ________ travels ________ than sound.

KEY POINTS

- Sound travels faster in solids than it does in water or air.
- Light travels much faster than sound.

L3 HOW DO WE HEAR SOUNDS?

How do we hear?

Sounds make the air in your ears vibrate. This makes parts inside the ear vibrate. The ear turns the vibrations into nerve impulses, which go to the brain. The brain then translates these messages into the words, music and sounds that you hear.

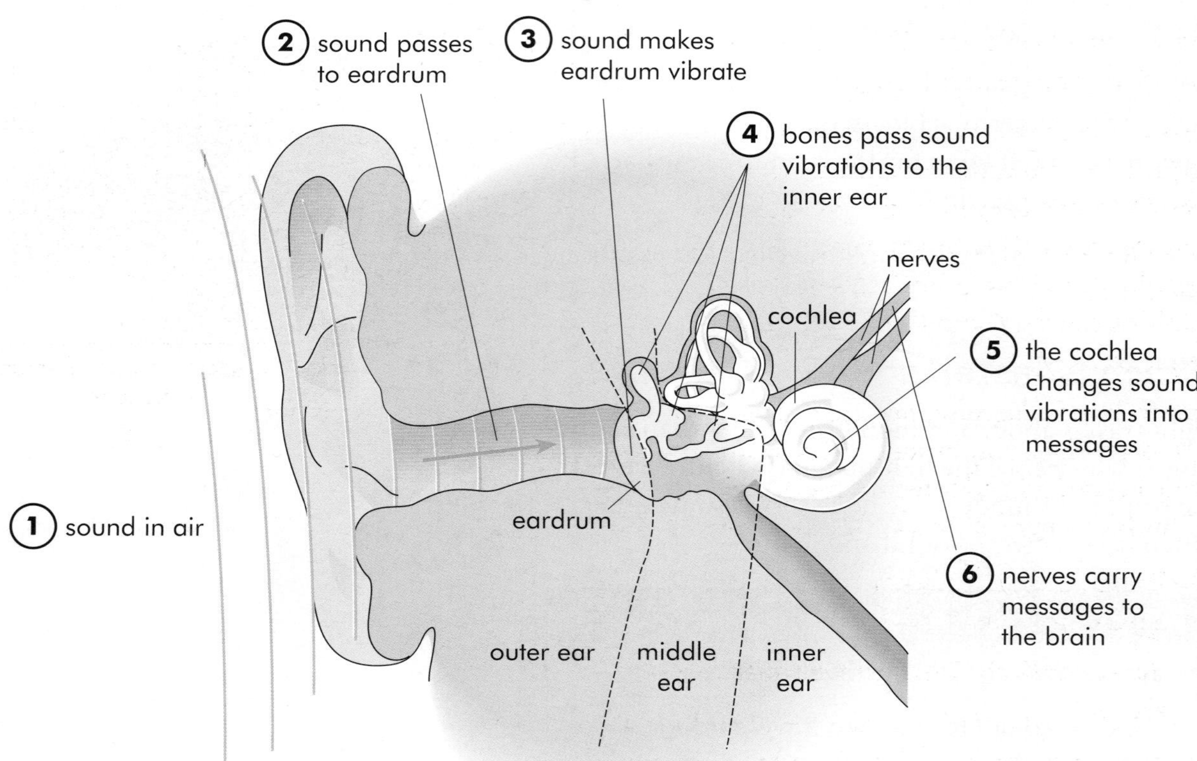
2 sound passes to eardrum
3 sound makes eardrum vibrate
4 bones pass sound vibrations to the inner ear
nerves
cochlea
5 the cochlea changes sound vibrations into messages
1 sound in air
eardrum
6 nerves carry messages to the brain
outer ear
middle ear
inner ear

What can we hear?

The lowest frequency that we can hear is about 20 vibrations per second. We call this 20 Hz for short. The highest frequency that we can hear is about 20 000 vibrations per second. We call this 20 000 Hz for short.

a **What is the lowest and highest frequency that we can hear?**

What happens when we get older?

As people get older their hearing gets worse. Look at the chart. The lower the line, the worse is the hearing.

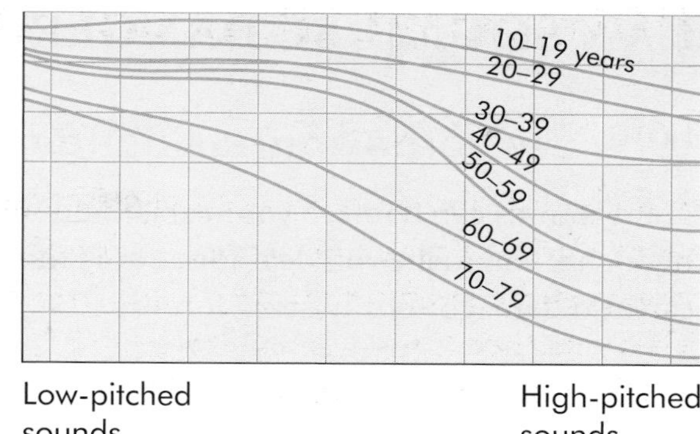

b **Who will have poorer hearing, a 10-year-old or a 70-year-old?**

What can animals hear?

Some sounds are too high and we can't hear them. Some sounds are too low and we can't hear them. The sounds are outside our range of hearing.

Look at the chart. It shows the sound frequencies that different animals can hear. Dogs can hear higher frequencies than we can. This is why they can hear a dog whistle and we can't. Bats and dolphins can hear sounds of a very high frequency.

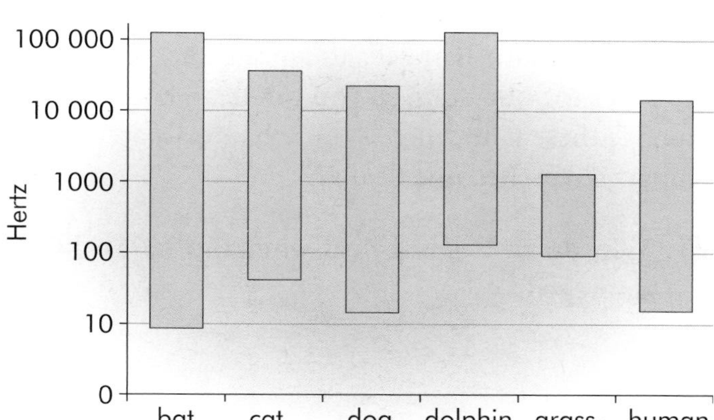

Bats are blind. They use their ears instead of their eyes to find their way around. They send out very high-frequency sound and listen for the **echoes**. The echoes tell the bats where objects are so they don't fly into them.

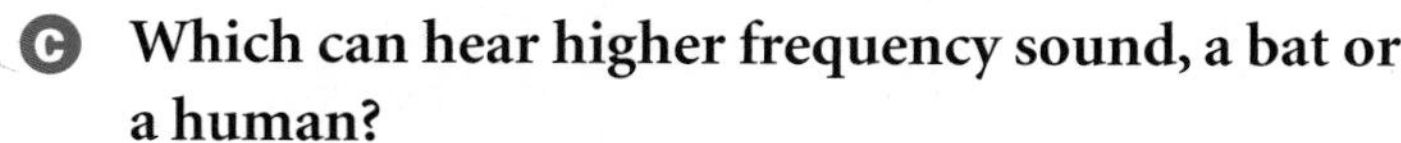

c **Which can hear higher frequency sound, a bat or a human?**

d **Bats are blind. How do they find their way around?**

Elephants use low-frequency sound to communicate with each other. It is so low that we cannot hear it.

QUESTIONS

Copy these sentences and fill in the spaces using the words below:

frequencies   smaller   20

Humans hear sound between ________ Hz and 20 000 Hz. As we get older, the range we can hear gets ________ . Animals hear sound of different ________ from humans.

KEY POINTS

- We hear sounds because they make parts of our ears vibrate.
- Humans hear sound between 20 Hz and 20 000 Hz. This range gets smaller as we get older.
- Animals hear sounds of different frequencies from humans.

CAN SOUND BE DANGEROUS?

Why are some sounds dangerous?

Loud sounds can damage your ears. Loud music at a nightclub can make you deaf for a short time. But it can also damage your hearing forever.

Look at the picture. It shows some nerve endings inside your ear. The nerve endings are attached to very fine hair cells.

Sound causes the hair cells to vibrate and send messages to your brain so you can hear. Loud sounds damage these hair cells. As more hair cells are damaged, you become deafer.

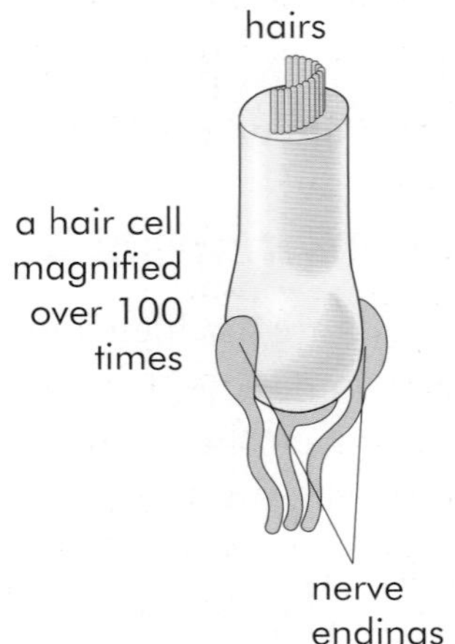

a **Why do we become deaf when our hair cells are damaged?**

What is noise pollution?

Noise pollution is any loud, annoying sounds. Lots of things can cause noise pollution.

- Aircraft taking off and landing at an airport. People living very close to airports can suffer from noise pollution.
- Road workers using road drills. The noise can be very loud so the workers have to wear ear protection.
- Noisy neighbours. It may not be loud enough to damage your hearing, but it can be a nuisance when you are trying to get to sleep.

b **What is noise pollution?**

c **Name three examples of different types of noise pollution.**

How can we protect ourselves from noise?

The best way is to get rid of the noise. Unfortunately this is not always possible. Another way to protect ourselves is to use a material that absorbs sound. These materials are called **insulating** materials. Examples of insulating materials include:

- double glazing
- cavity wall insulation
- carpets and curtains.

Sound barriers are another good way to reduce noise pollution. Look at the picture. The house is next to a noisy motorway. A sound barrier has been built between the house and the motorway. This makes the sound waves travel upwards and not towards the house.

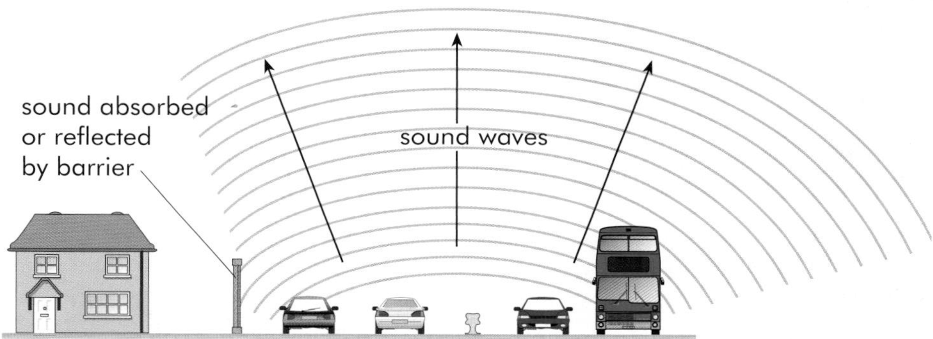

d **How can we stop noise pollution from a motorway?**

QUESTIONS

Copy these sentences and fill in the spaces using the words below:

damage insulating pollution

Loud sounds can permanently ________ your ears. A loud or annoying noise is called noise ________ . We can protect ourselves from noise pollution by using ________ materials.

KEY POINTS

- Loud sounds can permanently damage your ears.
- Loud or annoying noise can cause noise pollution.
- We can protect ourselves from noise pollution by using insulating materials.

L5 INVESTIGATING SOUND

Why two ears?

Humans, like most other animals, have two ears. This is so we can detect from which direction a sound is coming.

We can show this by doing an experiment. Eleanor is our volunteer. She is blindfolded so she cannot see. She must keep her head very still. A bell is rung in different positions around her head. Eleanor has to point to where she thinks the sound is coming from. The experiment is repeated with an ear defender on one of Eleanor's ears.

Eleanor finds that it is much easier to work out where sound is coming from when she uses both of her ears.

a **Why do humans have two ears?**

Can people with big ears hear better?

If we didn't have outer ears, we would still be able to hear. But we might miss quiet sounds. The outer ear reflects sounds into the inner ear. Cupping your hand around the outer ear helps even more.

b **Why is Eleanor cupping her hand around her outer ear?**

Eleanor decided to do an experiment. She wanted to know if the size of a person's outer ear affected how well they could hear.

The prediction

She predicted that people with larger ears could hear quieter sounds.

What to measure

To calculate the ear size she measured the height and width of the ear. She then multiplied these two numbers together to get an ear size.

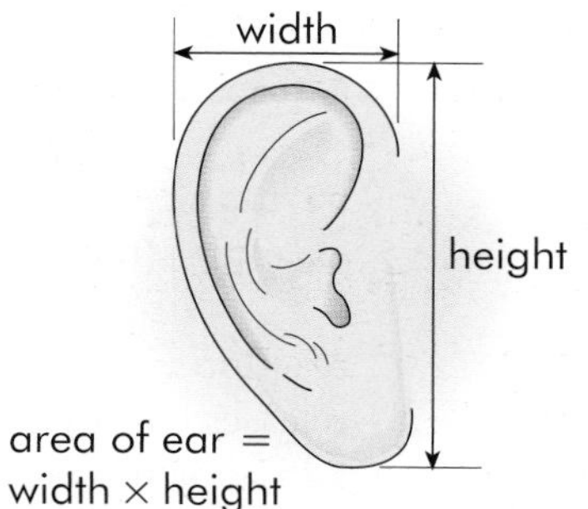

What to keep the same

She used people of the same sex and age. She did the experiment at the same time of day. She also made sure that she used sound of the same frequency, distance and direction.

Her results

Her results showed that people with bigger ears could hear fainter sounds.

Her evaluation

She asked other students in her class to repeat her experiment to see if they got the same results. This helped her see if her experiment was accurate.

Solving noise pollution

Read this case study.

> **Case study**
> A factory that makes metal biscuit boxes opened a new building. People who lived nearby complained about a high-pitched noise. They said it was made by some of the metal-grinding machines.

C **Suggest three ways the factory owners could reduce noise pollution for the people who live nearby. Explain how your ideas would work.**

Glossary

absorption digested **nutrients** pass through the walls of the **small intestine** into the **blood**

accumulation the process of building up or gathering together

acidic having a pH less than 7, for example **stomach** acid

aerobic respiration reaction in living things that releases **energy** using **glucose** and oxygen

agar jelly jelly used in a **Petri dish** to provide food for growing **microbes**

alkaline having a pH greater than 7

alveoli air sacs in the lungs where **gas exchange** happens

amplitude the size of a vibration

amylase **enzyme** that breaks down **starch**

anaerobic respiration reactions in living things that release **energy** without using oxygen

animal kingdom large group of organisms that do not make their own food but eat other organisms

antibiotic chemical that kills **bacteria**, used inside the body as a medicine

antibodies chemicals made by **white blood cells** to kill **microbes**

anus the end point of the **digestive system** where the waste leaves

arteries **blood vessels** that carry **blood** away from the **heart**

atom the smallest bit of something

attract pull towards something

bacteria **microbes** that have cells without a nucleus

balanced diet **diet** that provides the range of **nutrients** you need to stay healthy

bar magnet rectangular magnet with a pole at each end

basalt **igneous rock** with small crystals

bleaches removes the colour from something

blood fluid that transports substances around the body

blood vessels tubes that carry **blood** around the body

body temperature the usual **temperature** that the body stays at, in humans 37 °C

boiling point the **temperature** at which a **pure** substance changes from a liquid to a gas

calcium carbonate **mineral** found in limestone and other rocks, which reacts with acid

capillaries small **blood vessels** with thin walls, which carry **blood** between **arteries** and **veins**

carbohydrate group of **nutrients** that provide a quick source of **energy**

cement material that 'glues' rock **grains** together

cementation the process of 'gluing' rock **grains** together

change of state material changing **state** between solid, liquid or gas

chemical change a change that forms a new substance

chemical digestion **digestion** of food which involves **enzymes** and makes new substances

chemical formula symbols and numbers used for short to represent a chemical **compound**

chemical reaction another name for a **chemical change**

chemical weathering changing a rock by **chemical reactions**

circulation the **blood** moves round and round the body in **blood vessels**

classifying putting things into groups

cobalt an **element** that is a magnetic metal

community all the different organisms living in a **habitat**

compaction the process of squashing rocks

compound a **pure** substance made of two or more types of **atom** that are chemically joined

conduction movement of **energy** through a solid

conductor material that is good at letting **energy** pass through it, such as heat, sound or electricity

consumers animals, which must eat other living things for food

contracts gets shorter and thinner

convection liquids or gases moving due to differences in **temperature** and **density**

convection current flow of liquids or gases due to **convection**

cystic fibrosis inherited disease which affects breathing

degrees Celsius (°C) unit for **temperature**

delta flat area where a river flows in lots of streams to the sea over **deposits** of **sediments**

density how much mass is in a certain space

deposition **sediments** are put down or dropped, for example on a river bed

diet the **nutrients** that you eat

digestion the process by which food is broken down into smaller particles

digestive system the organs involved in **digestion**

disinfectant chemical that kills **microbes**, used outside the body

Earth's magnetic field **magnetic field** around the Earth

echo	sound reflected off a surface
ecosystem	the **habitat** and all the living things that live there
electromagnet	magnet formed by electric current passing through a coil around a wire
elements	the simplest substances, made up of only one type of **atom**
energy transfer	**energy** moving from one place to another
energy	the ability to make things happen
environmental conditions	conditions in a **habitat** which affect what can survive there
enzymes	chemicals found in the **digestive system**, which break down large **nutrient** particles into smaller ones
epidemic	when lots of people have the same disease at the same time
equation	a way of writing something that is easy for different people to understand
evaporation	**change of state** from liquid to gas at the surface of a liquid
evaporite rock	rock formed when a lake evaporates and leaves the dissolved **minerals** behind
expands	gets longer and thicker
fat	**nutrient** used as an **energy** store
fermentation	breakdown of a substance by **bacteria** or **yeast,** usually without oxygen
fibre	indigestible food which keeps your **digestive system** working properly
food chain	picture showing what an animal eats and what eats it
food web	picture made of lots of joined up **food chains**, showing what eats what in a **habitat** and the flow of **energy** in the habitat
fossils	remains of plant or animal material found in rock
freezing	changing from liquid to solid state
frequency	how often something happens
fungi	**microbes** that can be different sizes; some have many cells with nuclei joined together
gas exchange	when oxygen passes into the **blood** and carbon dioxide moves out of the blood; takes place in **alveoli**
geologist	a scientist who studies the Earth
glucose	a **carbohydrate** with small particles, used by the body to give **energy**
grains	the small fragments or crystals that make up a rock
granite	**igneous rock** with big crystals
grow	increase in size
gullet	tube that carries food from the **mouth** to the **stomach** in the **digestive system**
habitat	the place where an animal or plant lives
heart	organ that pumps **blood** around the body

igneous rocks	rocks formed from molten (melted) material
immune	**antibodies** already in your **blood** recognise **microbes** and stop them causing disease
immunisation	injecting a **vaccine** to make you **immune** to a disease
incident ray	light ray that hits a surface
infection	having a **microbe** present in your body, which usually makes you ill
infectious	being able to pass on a disease
insulator, insulating	material that is a very poor **conductor** of energy, such as heat, electricity or sound
lactic acid	substance formed in **anaerobic respiration**, which causes aching muscles
large intestine	organ in the **digestive system** where water is absorbed
lateral inversion	objects appear back to front, as when reflected in a mirror
lens	part of the eye that focuses light onto the **retina**
luminous	gives off light
magma	molten rock underground
magnetic	a substance that is affected by a magnet
magnetic field	region where there is a magnetic force
magnetic field lines	lines showing which way a **magnetic north pole** would move
mechanical digestion	**digestion** of food by physical action to break it into smaller pieces, for example chewing
medium	material that energy passes through, for example sound or light
melting	changing from solid to liquid state
melting point	the **temperature** at which a **pure** substance changes from a solid to a liquid
metamorphic rocks	rocks formed from other rocks changed by heat and pressure
microbes	tiny organisms that can be seen only under a microscope
microorganisms	another name for **microbes**
minerals (Unit A)	substances needed in the **diet** in small amounts to keep you healthy
minerals (Unit G)	substances found in rocks
mixture	two or more substances that are mixed together but not chemically joined
model	way of imagining how something works
molecule	group of **atoms** that are chemically joined
mouth	beginning of the **digestive system** where food enters the body
nickel	an **element** that is a **magnetic** metal
noise pollution	sound which is a nuisance
non-luminous	does not give out light

normal line at right angles to a surface

north pole end of a magnet that repels a north pole

nutrients substances in food that are needed and used by your body

observation things we see, feel or smell while we watch an experiment

opaque a material that does not allow light to pass through

pancreas organ in the **digestive system** that makes **enzymes** to digest food

pathogen organism that causes disease

penicillin first **antibiotic**, discovered by Sir Alexander Fleming

Periodic Table table showing all the **elements**

Petri dish flat dish with a lid, used for growing **microbes**

physical weathering breaking down a rock without making new substances

pitch how high or low a sound is

plant kingdom group of living things which make their food using light energy

plasma fluid part of **blood** which carries everything apart from oxygen around the body

population number of individuals of a species in an area at a certain time

porous rock with spaces between the **grains**

predator animal that hunts other animals for food

prescription form written by a doctor to get medicines, including antibiotics

prey animal that is hunted and eaten by another animal

primary colours three colours seen by the human eye

primary consumer first animal in a **food chain**; it eats the producer

prism triangular block of glass

producers plants, which produce their own food using **energy** from the Sun

properties the characteristics of a substance

protein **nutrient** needed for growth

pupil hole in the eye that allows light in

pure not mixed with anything else

pyramid of numbers picture showing the numbers of organisms at each level of a **food chain**

quadrat frame that measures 1 m^2, used for **sampling**

radiation **energy** moving without the need for a **medium** to pass through

ray diagram picture that shows which way light rays travel

rectum where waste food is stored in the **digestive system** before leaving through the **anus**

red blood cells cells in the **blood** that carry oxygen around the body

reflected ray light ray that bounces off a surface

reflection light bouncing off a surface in an organised way

refraction light bending when it passes from one material to another

repel push something away

resistant **bacteria** that are not affected by **antibiotics**

retina light-sensitive surface at the back of the eye

rickets disease caused by a lack of vitamin D in the **diet**

rock cycle way (such as a picture) of linking the processes that form rocks

salt common name for **sodium chloride**

sampling method of estimating the size of the **population**

scattered disorganisation of light

secondary consumer the second animal in a **food chain**; it eats the **primary consumer**

sedimentary rocks rocks formed from **deposited** rock fragments

sediments fragments of broken rock

sexually transmitted disease disease caused by **microbes** passed on to others during sexual intercourse

shadow area of darkness where light is blocked by an object

small intestine organ in the **digestive system** where food is digested and absorbed

sodium silvery metallic **element** that reacts violently with water

sodium chloride the chemical name for salt

source place where light or heat comes from

south pole end of a magnet that attracts a **north pole**

spectrum the range of colours in white light

starch a **carbohydrate** found in rice and potatoes

state of matter the three states of matter are solid, liquid and gas

stomach organ in the **digestive system** where food is mashed and mixed with enzymes

symbol sign that means something

temperature how hot or cold a material is

texture the way that rock **grains** fit together

thermal energy heat **energy** in a material

thermometer used for measuring **temperature**

trachea tube that takes air into the lungs

translucent material that **scatters** light as the light passes through it

transmission (Unit K) light passing through a material

transmitted (Unit C) **microbes** are passed from one person to another

transparent material that allows light to pass through without **scattering**

transport	the process of moving rock fragments from one place to another
vaccine	substance put into your **blood** to make you **immune** to certain **microbes**
vacuum	space with no material in it
vegetarians	people who do not eat meat
veins	**blood vessels** that carry **blood** towards the **heart**
vibrating	moving backwards and forwards rapidly
viruses	tiny **microbes** that invade cells and cause disease
vitamins	substances needed in the **diet** in small amounts to keep you healthy
weathering	changing a rock by natural processes
white blood cells	cells in the **blood** which defend the body against **infection**
word equation	a way of recording a **chemical reaction**
yeast	**fungus** used to make bread and wine

Index

Note: page numbers for **glossary** definitions are in **bold**.